"Are you going to look for a more suitable lover?"

Rose snorted. "What's a more suitable lover?" she demanded tartly.

"Someone like me."

The audacity of it took her breath away.

"You're not serious?" She faltered.

"On the contrary, I'm intensely serious. I want you, Rose Ashley. And I always get what I want."

ANGELA DEVINE grew up in Tasmania, Australia, surrounded by forests, mountains and wild seas, so she dislikes big cities. Before taking up writing, she worked as a teacher, librarian and university lecturer. As a young mother and Ph.D. student, she read romance fiction for fun and later decided it would be even more fun to write it. She is married, with four children, loves chocolate and Twinings teas and hates ironing. Her current hobbies are gardening, bushwalking, traveling and classical music.

Books by Angela Devine

HARLEQUIN PRESENTS
1538—WIFE FOR A NIGHT
1621—SEED OF THE FIRE LILY

ANGELA DEVINE

Dark Pirate

Harlequin Books

TORONTO • NEW YORK • LONDON
AMSTERDAM • PARIS • SYDNEY • HAMBURG
STOCKHOLM • ATHENS • TOKYO • MILAN
MADRID • WARSAW • BUDAPEST • AUCKLAND

ISBN 0-373-18671-1

DARK PIRATE

First North American Publication 1998.

Printed in U.S.A.

CHAPTER ONE

ROSE had never seen a man who looked quite so dangerous as the fisherman lounging at the table opposite her. At least, she presumed he was a fisherman because the snatches of conversation that drifted to her above the hubbub of the bar were all concerned with fishing. Yet he might just as well have been a Cornish smuggler right out of the past with that thick, glossy black hair, chocolate-brown eyes and brooding features. He must have been in his mid-thirties and he had the tough, lawless look of a smuggler. In this village where time stood still it was easy to imagine a man like that striding ashore by the fitful light of the moon with a brandy barrel slung carelessly over one powerful shoulder. Or leading a lusty brawl against the Excise men, striking out with his clenched fists and revelling in the danger and the excitement. It was also easy to imagine him in a darkened doorway, hauling a village girl into a fierce embrace and kissing her until she was dizzy with longing. There was something about the feral glint in his eyes and the lurking sensuality about the corners of his mouth that told Rose he knew a lot about women. Even his old clothes could not diminish his air of power and sensuality. He wore faded blue jeans and a red checked flannel shirt with the sleeves rolled up, revealing muscular arms covered in coarse, dark hair. Not designer elegance by any stretch of the imagination, yet the aura of confidence and vibrant animal magnetism that radiated out from him was almost indecent in its intensity.

5

I wonder if he's married, thought Rose. Suddenly she became aware that his chocolate-brown eyes were fixed on her and that the sardonic smile on his lips was growing a little wider. Horrified at being caught staring so rudely, Rose dropped her gaze, but she could not restrain the tide of colour that flushed hotly into her cheeks. There was the scraping sound of a chair being pushed back, light, prowling footsteps approached and then he was standing beside her. So close that she could feel the warmth emanating from his body in waves, smell the clean, masculine scent of him, compounded of salt air and a soap that reminded her of leather, could see the thrust of his hard, muscular thighs against the fabric of his jeans.

'Can I get you a drink, my love?' he murmured and the voice was as devastating as the rest of him—a deep, soft, Cornish burr with that alarming intimacy that all Cornish speech seemed to hold, a slow, confiding cadence that made her feel as if even total strangers were welcoming her as their closest friend. 'I'm just getting another beer for Charlie and me, so it'll be no trouble if you'd like something.'

Was it an attempt to pick her up or merely a sociable gesture, natural in such a small village? Rose darted a swift glance of alarm at him, wishing the floor would open up and swallow her. Close up, he was even more disturbing with his even white teeth and those tiny pale lines around his eyes contrasting with his tan. She had seen men like that in Australia, men who spent long hours outdoors, screwing up their eyes in bright sunlight and gazing keenly through immense distances. He looked down at her with a mocking, unhurried manner as if he could read every thought in her head and was vastly amused by them. Then he transferred the second beer mug into his left hand and held out his other hand for her glass. Rose, who had been staring at him in a frozen way, suddenly came to life and clapped both her hands protectively over it.

'No! Really. It's all right. Thank you very much, it's awfully kind of you, but I must be going soon. I'll just finish this and then . . .' Her voice trailed away.

'Just as you like,' he agreed amiably and turned away towards the bar.

Rose gazed after his broad back with the feeling that she had just made an appalling fool of herself. A small, unsteady sigh escaped her and she poured the last inch or so of sparkling apple cider into her glass and sipped it slowly in an attempt to calm her nerves. What was wrong with her? After all, she was twenty-seven years old, not some giggling teenager. And with several years' experience as a highly paid and respected computer programmer, she was used to dealing with tough male executives, men who didn't respect any woman unless she proved she could hold her own. And Rose could. Not only was she good at her job, but she had also learnt all the social skills that went with it: the cool, poised manner, the power dressing, the hairstyles that confined her long, unruly chestnut curls in a neat chignon or a smooth braid. Above all, she had learnt to feel as if she was in control of her life.

So how could this flamboyant Cornish fisherman simply offer to buy her a drink and give her palpitations as if she were a silly schoolgirl? It must be because she was still upset about Martin's betrayal and therefore acting totally out of character. Or perhaps it was just the atmosphere of Polperro itself—so quaint, so serene, so olde-worlde that it woke an impulsive, romantic part of her nature that had lain buried most of her life. After all, how else could she explain her decision only this morning to buy a wildly expensive cream knitted sweater hand-embroidered with tiny flowers and a swirling muslin skirt to match? A fairly amazing departure from her

usual tailored suits like the one she was wearing now!
But somehow the outfit had felt exactly right when she
had tried it on. The pale blue forget-me-nots had
matched the colour of her eyes and, moved by an odd
instinct, she had unclipped the gold slide which had
pinned her hair severely at the nape of her neck and let
it spring free in wavy brown profusion around her
shoulders. The unfamiliar image of herself as soft,
wistful, feminine had been irresistible. She had put down
a small deposit and asked the shopkeeper to hold the
clothes until she could go to the bank and cash some
traveller's cheques to pay for them... That thought gave
her a jolt. Oh, help! What time did the banks close?
Rose forgot all about Cornish fishermen and glanced
down at her watch in alarm. She would have to hurry!

Unzipping her bag, she reached into the compartment
where she kept her red vinyl pocketbook containing her
traveller's cheques. Her fingers groped in vain. The first
uneasy stirring began inside her and she glanced sharply
down. There was no sign of her pocketbook, but it must
be here, it must! Everything of importance was in it—
her passport, her traveller's cheques, her return airline
ticket to Australia. Frantically she began to unzip the
other navy leather compartments. A map of Cornwall,
a roll of Polo mints, a neatly pressed white handkerchief, a pocket diary and pen, a comb, lipstick, the keys
to Aunt Em's cottage. But no pocketbook. Rose felt a
sudden chill lurch of panic and dismay in the pit of her
stomach as if she had stepped off the edge of a cliff.
Her normally pink cheeks were suddenly drained of
colour and she let out an involuntary gasp. The fisherman
was looming beside her in an instant.

'What's the matter, my dear? You've gone quite pale.
Are you ill?'

'N-no,' stammered Rose. 'But I've lost my
pocketbook. It's got everything in it. My passport, my

traveller's cheques, my airline ticket... Oh, what am I going to do? I've lost everything except my little money purse and that's only got fifty pence in it!'

'Now don't take on,' said the man mildly. 'Polperro's a small village and folks here are very honest, unless one of those tourists has got their hands on it. Still, like as not, what's happened is this: you've taken it out of your bag somewhere to pay for something and not fastened the bag properly, then it's fallen out. It's happened to me before today. Now you just try and think, my dear. When did you have it last?'

Rose tried to control the churning sensation in her stomach long enough to allow her to concentrate. She had arrived by bus from Looe at about eleven o'clock, then she had taken a horse-drawn carriage from the head of the gorge to the centre of the village. After that she had spent a couple of hours exploring all the quaint little alleyways with their tea-shops and art galleries and souvenirs. And there had been a small clothing shop near the harbour... It was there that she had fallen hopelessly in love with the sweater and skirt and paid a deposit on them. The woman at the shop had not wanted to take traveller's cheques, but had directed her to a bank where she could cash them. Not wanting too many parcels to carry, Rose had decided to postpone her visit to the bank until the afternoon. Several hours had been spent happily ambling around the old cottages and shops, some with whorls in their glass windows, others with patterns of shells set into their limewashed walls, spending most of her cash on postcards and souvenirs. She had also taken a walk up the cliff path and she seemed to remember seeing the red vinyl cover of the pocketbook poking up in her bag when she had put a handkerchief away...

'On the cliff-top, I think,' she said, frowning thought-fully. 'But I've walked all over the place since then. It could be anywhere.'

She explained haltingly about the clothes at the shop by the harbour, her intended visit to the bank, the way she had wandered about. Impatiently her companion cut her off.

'Well, let's begin by seeing if you've dropped it here,' he suggested practically. 'Come on, I'll help you.'

Rose was too preoccupied to disagree, but she did find it rather surprising that the stranger had taken charge with such firmness and efficiency, even if his manner was a trifle curt. Why was he doing this? Was it simple kindness or some other motive? Oh, what did it matter? The important thing was to find her pocketbook.

They both fell to their knees and searched the floor under the table, but it was quite clear that there was nothing there. As she got to her feet Rose felt a hu-miliating rush of tears sting her eyes. After all the trauma of resigning from her job, leaving Martin, her mother's sudden need for a hysterectomy as they were due to leave Australia and then the gruelling flight to England, this was the last thing that she needed! Swallowing hard, she made a blind movement as if to turn away.

'Thank you for looking,' she said unsteadily. 'I suppose I'll just have to report it to the police as missing and phone American Express. Oh, I wish this hadn't happened!' Her voice broke on the last words and the stranger gave an exasperated sigh, put his warm, mus-cular hands on her shoulders and steered her into a chair. The kindness of the action surprised her. He didn't look like a man who would be kind. There was something too ruthless about the set of his chin, the narrowed eyes, the tough mouth. Yet here he was, calming her down, with only the slightest hint of impatience in his manner—

a faint curl of his lips that made her feel she was making far too much fuss about a very trivial event...

'Now, don't you worry,' he ordered sternly. 'We'll soon have this sorted out. Sit down there and I'll get you another drink, and then we'll decide what we're going to do. What would you like?'

'I haven't got any money——' began Rose, but found herself silenced by three strong brown fingers placed over her lips.

'I don't suppose I'll go broke on the price of one drink,' the man said sardonically. 'Now, what will you have?'

Rose made a small, choking sound that was closer to a giggle than a sob, then blew her nose and straightened her shoulders.

'A non-alcoholic cider, please,' she said.

Her eyes followed him as he moved away to the bar. There was a negligent, animal grace about his movements that made him look totally appropriate in this setting. A wild, lawless Cornishman if ever there was one! And how different from Martin, whose aggression so often dwindled to mere bluster... Yet somehow there was a savage aura of controlled power about this Cornishman that made Martin seem boastful and florid in comparison. He must draw women to him as relentlessly as moths to a naked flame. Well, she wasn't fool enough to be burnt a second time. All the same, an uneasy tingle of excitement sparked through Rose's body as she watched the stranger striding back from the bar with her drink. He set it down in front of her and then stretched out his hand.

'I'm Greg Trelawney,' he announced. 'One of the locals. And who are you?'

'I'm Rose. Rose Ashley,' she replied, feeling slightly unnerved by the warm, firm clasp of those fingers. It was as if a powerful electric current had surged through her at his touch. 'I'm from Australia.'

'Welcome to Polperro,' he said, raising his glass. 'Although I'm sorry your welcome has been such a poor one. Well, we'll see what we can do to sort that out in a minute. Now have a drink and catch your breath. Cheers!'

'Cheers!' agreed Rose.

The sweet, sparkling cider with its strong taste of apples did help to revive Rose, but, even more than that, the presence of the man opposite her had the effect of distracting her from her immediate problems. How could she concentrate on a lost pocketbook when Greg Trelawney was gazing at her with that intent, brooding expression?

'Now, tell me about this pocketbook of yours,' he urged when at last she had emptied her glass. 'You say you had it last on the cliff-top?'

'Yes,' agreed Rose.

He pushed away his empty glass and rose to his feet.

'Well, we'd better go up on the cliffs and look for it,' he announced briskly. 'Chances are you've dropped it somewhere and it'll soon be found. Folks here are very honest, you know. I reckon we'll turn it up in the next hour or so.'

'Oh, but you don't have to help me,' protested Rose. 'I can't possibly take up so much of your time.'

He gave a low growl of laughter at that. A laugh that reverberated in his chest and made his dark eyes glint.

'I'm not busy. I've finished for the day and I'd be better off helping you than wasting my time and money in a pub. Eh, Jimmy?'

'That's right, Greg,' agreed the barman. 'You give the lass a hand and don't you worry, my dear. If so be as you don't find 'un, you come back here and we'll sort something out.'

Rose darted a stricken look from one man to the other. Of course she wanted to find the pocketbook and the sooner the better. But she wasn't at all sure that she wanted to tramp around cliff paths with a man who made her feel like a lovelorn teenager. Still, what else could she do?

'Thank you,' she said at last in a strained voice. 'I'll do that.'

The Smuggler's Rest was only a few steps away from the precipitous path which led up over the rocks to the cliff-top. Greg bounded up the steep slope like a mountain goat, so that Rose had to hurry to keep him in sight. It was a stiff climb, with jagged brown rocks jutting out into the path and pink erigeron daisies spilling out from cottage gardens. As they neared the top of the path, the dry-stone walls which marked the boundaries of neatly tended gardens gave way to a wild landscape of breathtaking beauty. Only the distant line of the horizon marked out the division between the vivid dark blue of the sea and the paler blue of the sky. Overhead the sun shone with an almost Mediterranean heat, gilding the wings of an occasional gliding seagull and warming the rocks that flanked the path. Down below waves smashed noisily against the cliff face and fell back in a seething white turbulence of foam.

Shading her eyes against the brilliance of the sun, Rose gazed down at the Net Loft—a dry-stone building on the cliff at the west side of the harbour entrance, its walls fashioned from mellow grey stone smudged with yellow-green lichen. For a moment she stood still, hot and breathless from the climb and momentarily distracted from her worries by the beauty of the scene. Seagulls wheeled and shrieked overhead and the air was charged with enticing scents—brown earth as rich as chocolate fudge and with the same sweet, heavy smell, gorse bushes in full flower and the bracing salt tang of the sea. What an amazing place this was! But Greg seemed oblivious to the setting and was clearly impatient of her delay.

'Right, where did you go when you were up here?' he demanded.

'I sat on the bench over there for a while,' she said, wrinkling her forehead thoughtfully. 'And then I went for a walk further up the cliff.'

A search of the tussocky green grass beaded with raindrops in the area around the bench revealed nothing, so Greg set off further up the cliff path. Here the manicured cottage gardens gave way to wire netting tangled with blackberries, ivy, dock and thick stands of stinging nettles. As they reached the gorse bushes on the headland a cloud of orange and brown butterflies rose at their approach, but there was no sign of a pocketbook on the ground where Rose had stood earlier to admire the view. Greg searched thoroughly, but at last came back to her, shaking his head.

'Well, that's it, then,' she said heavily. 'I don't suppose I'll ever see it again.'

In spite of her good intentions she could not keep a faint tremor out of her voice. What was wrong with her? After all, she wasn't dead or injured. The events of the last two months must have been more of a strain than she realised. To her surprise, Greg suddenly caught one of her tendrils of long brown hair that was fluttering in the breeze and wound it round the end of his finger. Rose stiffened at his touch, although it was undoubtedly friendly rather than threatening. All the same, she darted him a swift, nervous glance as he tidied the errant strand back over her shoulder.

'Well, it's not the end of the world,' he said with a touch of his earlier impatience. 'Just come back to the pub with me and we'll report it missing. After that we can see about getting you back to your hotel.'

'Hotel!' wailed Rose, as the realisation of a fresh disaster suddenly struck her. 'What's the time?'

'Four thirty-five.'

'Oh, no! I've missed the bus!'

'Bus?' queried Greg. 'Where were you going to?'

'Pisky Bay,' replied Rose.

'Pisky Bay?' he demanded, his brows meeting in a thoughtful frown. 'Are you sure? There's nothing there but three or four cottages.'

'I know,' agreed Rose. 'Actually, I'm the new owner of one of them. My great-aunt Em died recently and left it to me.'

A look of dawning comprehension spread over his craggy features.

'Oh, then you'll be Emily Pendennis's great-niece,' he said. 'Yes, I heard she'd left her cottage to a lass from foreign parts. But wasn't there talk of your mother coming here as well?'

Rose gave a wry smile at the efficiency with which the bush telegraph seemed to be operating. After the vast, impersonal sprawl of Brisbane, she found it strangely warming to find a community so intimate that everyone knew each other's business. Far from being annoyed by it, she was oddly moved.

'That's right,' she admitted. 'My mother was supposed to come with me, but unfortunately she was taken ill just before we were due to leave Brisbane. Nothing really serious, but she had to have an operation and my insurance policy wouldn't allow me to cancel my airline ticket. In any case, my mother urged me to come and she'll be joining me in a few weeks, as soon as she's well enough to travel. We're hoping to open a bed-and-breakfast place in Aunt Em's old cottage.'

'You'll be staying on here, then?' asked Greg, and for an instant something disturbingly sensual lurked in his eyes.

Rose might be alarmed by that momentary spark of warmth but she couldn't help feeling flattered by it. In all the three years she had spent with Martin, he had only seemed to make her aware of her deficiencies, that her nose was too snub, her hips too rounded, her legs too short, her skin too pale. Now, with this rugged fisherman darting her a swift sideways glance from under half-closed lids, Rose suddenly felt that she was a desirable woman. The thought sent a flood of colour rushing into her cheeks and made her step back a pace from him.

'Yes,' she muttered. 'At least for a while.'

'Well, that's good news,' he said mildly. 'If there's anything I can do to help you out, just say the word. This is only a simple fishing community and we're all good neighbours hereabouts.'

If he had asked her to go out with him, Rose would have retreated in alarm and refused immediately. As it was, his manner was so casual that she began to think that she had imagined that brief flare of attraction between them. What an idiot she was! Obviously Greg was only trying to be kind...

'Oh, I'm sure you are,' she agreed with a rush of enthusiasm. 'This village seems absolutely enchanting and I'm thrilled to think that my roots here go back for centuries. You see, I've always hated big cities and wished I could live somewhere small and quaint. Well, I'd say Polperro is the kind of place that time has passed by, where people still enjoy old-fashioned pleasures. Going fishing, gardening, spending time with their friends, having a quiet drink in the pub. I can almost imagine that I'm still in the eighteenth century here. Actually, when I first saw you I thought you looked exactly like——' She broke off and flushed with embarrassment, aware that his eyes were on her with a frankly amazed expression.

'Like what?' he prompted in his husky Cornish voice.

'Like a smuggler,' she admitted.

Suddenly he threw back his head and laughed, an incredulous, pitying laugh that made her feel a complete fool.

'I'm sorry,' she said in confusion. 'I suppose it sounds silly really.'

An expression mid-way between contempt and amusement flitted across his face.

'You're not far out, in a way,' he replied. 'Just between you and me, in my youth there was the odd bottle of brandy I brought back on my fishing boat from France that never paid duty in any Customs office.'

'You're a fisherman, then!' she exclaimed with interest. 'I thought you must be. You looked like one, somehow. Exactly the way I imagined a Cornish fisherman.'

'Ah, well, my dear,' he said. 'It's clear you're a romantic at heart and I've always liked the romantic, myself.' Was it her imagination or did his Cornish accent suddenly seem stronger than it had before? 'But tell me, now, how are you going to get home to your aunt Em's cottage, seeing you've missed the bus?'

Rose hesitated and then took the plunge.

'W-well,' she stammered. 'I hate to ask you this when you've already done so much for me, but could you possibly loan me some money for a taxi? I'll pay you back tom——'

But Greg was sorrowfully shaking his head.

'I'm sorry, my love,' he muttered. 'I don't think I can do that. A simple fisherman like me doesn't carry much money on him.' He reached into his back pocket, drew out a shabby wallet and looked at the three one-pound coins that lay forlornly in it. 'I'll tell you what, though. I could sail you home. How about that, now? I'll drop you off all right and tight in the cove at Pisky Bay.'

Rose hesitated, torn between delight and apprehension. To sail home through the sunset and catch her first glimpse of her cottage from out in those dazzling, sapphire seas! It would be perfect, absolutely perfect...
And yet was it wise to trust herself to Greg Trelawney? Not that he was likely to abduct her, but there were other kinds of danger that could be more subtly threatening. Like the danger of contracting an absurd, adolescent crush on a man who was quite likely to see her day in and day out in such a small community. She didn't want the pain or the humiliation of that. Really, it would be more sensible to refuse. Sensible! something inside her shrieked in outrage. Where has being sensible ever got you? You were being sensible waiting for Martin to propose, weren't you? Well? In that instant Rose flung caution to the winds and decided to live dangerously.

'Thank you,' she said firmly before she could change her mind. 'That would be wonderful. But are you sure it's not too much trouble?'

'No trouble at all, my dear. There be my boat just down there, see? Lying at anchor on the mooring.'

Rose followed his pointing finger down to the spot where a stately old ketch, with a black hull and red sails furled along its boom, lay tranquilly bobbing next to a pink buoy. By now the tide was turning and the water rippled as green as glass around the graceful vessel, making it shift and move as if it longed to be off.

'Come on,' ordered Greg. 'We'll just go down to the phone at the pub and report your belongings missing. Then we'll be off.'

Ten minutes later their mission was accomplished and they stood outside on the whitewashed steps in front of the Smuggler's Rest.

'What about your luggage?' asked Greg, struck by a sudden difficulty.

'I sent it on ahead on this morning's bus,' replied Rose. 'One of Aunt Em's old neighbours has been keeping an eye on the cottage and she promised to take delivery of it for me. Oh, there's one other thing, though. I must call into the clothes shop and tell the woman I can't take that sweater and skirt after all.'

'Don't you worry about that,' said Greg. 'I'll take care of it. I have to go round to the far side of the stream in any case to get my dinghy. Now, you walk down to the stone pier over there and wait for me. I'll bring the ketch to the foot of that iron ladder and pick you up. Can't say fairer than that!'

Rose firmly dismissed her last lingering doubts. 'All right, thank you,' she agreed.

Twenty minutes later they were heading out to sea with the sails flaring bright red in the slanting gold light of the sun. There was no sound but the slap of water against the hull, the singing of the wind in the rigging and the occasional noisy squabbling of a flock of seagulls. Rose found the slow dip and rise of the vessel immensely soothing and she heaved a deep sigh of pleasure. A brief smile flickered over Greg's face but he said nothing, apparently content to enjoy the scene around them without any need for words. He was standing at the yacht's wheel, his long, muscular legs braced apart and his sensitive fingers handling its blunt wooden spokes as tenderly as if they were alive. With his eyes narrowed against the blaze of the sinking sun and his hair blown into wild disorder by the wind, he looked like some primitive, timeless sailor, totally in harmony with the rugged coastline that had produced him. An aching, primeval need stabbed through Rose's entire body at the sight of him standing there so virile, so confident, so untamed. I could really fall for him in a big way, she thought and then gave a soft gasp of dismay at her own unruly instincts. Living dangerously was one thing; going right off her trolley was quite another.

'Everything all right?' he asked, looking over his shoulder at her.

'Yes, fine, thank you,' she agreed, grateful that he could not read her thoughts. Yet perhaps he could, for his eyes narrowed even further and he looked at her with that strange, assessing warmth that she had found so disconcerting on the cliff-top. Once again a tingling current of raw physical attraction seemed to pass between them.

'Why don't you come and take a turn at the wheel?' invited Greg, and his baritone voice was so husky, so caressing that the invitation seemed vaguely indecent.

Rose opened her mouth to refuse and then paused. She was being foolish, incredibly foolish. All this belief in nameless, animal passions lurking just below the surface might be only a product of her own fevered imagination. Greg would probably think she was crazy if she started acting like some skittish, wild creature and refusing a perfectly harmless invitation.

'All right, thanks,' she agreed, forcing herself to rise and clamber nervously across the sloping deck to join him. 'What do I do?'

'Just put your hands here on the wheel at ten to two. Then take a look straight down the centre of the ship and line up the prow with that headland over there. If she begins to fall away, turn the wheel a little to bring her back on course. Yes, that's fine.'

As he had spoken he had positioned himself behind her, putting his arms around her and gripping her hands so that he could guide them. Harmless invitation! thought Rose despairingly. I didn't know he was going to do that! Her senses reeled at his overpowering nearness and her heart begun to beat in a frantic, suffocating rhythm. She was intensely conscious of his towering height, the power of the whipcord muscles in those strong tanned arms that were wrapped around her, the salty masculine smell that came off in waves from his warm body. For one insane moment she wondered what he would do if she suddenly leaned back against him. The mere thought made her go rigid with panic.

'I think you can let go now,' she said in a stifled voice.

Greg released her, but he continued to stand just behind her so that she found it difficult to keep her attention on handling the boat. Almost before she realised it, the bow began to stray out towards the open sea and Greg had to move forward to correct their course.

'I'll just help you out as we go down the channel between this rocky island up ahead and the mainland,' he explained. 'It looks as though there's plenty of space, but in fact there are some sharp reefs below the surface here. No, there's no need for you to move. All you have to do is let yourself go and trust me.'

But Rose had already wriggled free of his grip and was retreating to the safety of her seat in the stern. 'You'd better do it,' she said shakily. 'I'm afraid of running into disaster.'

A soft chuckle escaped him, but he did not argue with her. Rose looked out at the island looming ahead of them and tried to distract herself from Greg by examining every feature of it. It was nothing but a craggy outcrop of rock covered with bright emerald grass at the top and plummeting to wicked-looking rocky shores below. Seagulls whirled and shrieked above it and a mass of scudding clouds like shredded lace sent shadows chasing over its vivid green grass. Greg shaded his eyes and looked out at the restlessly heaving sea ablaze with light from the sinking sun.

'Not far to go now,' he announced in a matter-of-fact voice. 'Come by here and look. You see over there to starboard? That's Pisky Bay, just around the headland.'

The land began to come closer and closer and soon Rose could see a half-moon of sandy beach framed at each end by jagged cliffs. Emerald-green water rushed past her, then suddenly they were in the bay itself with the details of the land growing larger and sharper with every passing minute. Rose could not suppress a little cry of excitement as she saw a dusty road winding between hawthorn hedges, cows grazing placidly in a green field and three or four widely scattered cottages barely visible among the trees that surrounded them.

'Oh, I can hardly wait!' she exclaimed. 'Somehow I feel exactly as if I'm coming home!'

'Well, it won't be long now,' said Greg. 'I'll just take down the sails, drop anchor and I'll have you ashore in no time.'

He was as good as his word. A moment later the huge red mainsail came flapping down and was lashed securely around the boom, to be followed at once by the other two smaller sails. Then Greg hurried up to the bow of the yacht and there was a loud, grinding rattle as he let out the anchor chain. Then he came back along the narrow, polished deck of the yacht with the lithe tread of a hunting cat. Pausing with one hand on the entrance to the hatchway, he glanced back at Rose, his eyes narrowing in a way that made her heart beat faster.

'Are you planning to offer me a cup of tea when we get ashore?' he asked.

That was more than Rose had bargained for. Her whole body tensed in a useless impulse to retreat. 'I very much doubt it, I'm afraid. I have no idea of what I'm going to find once I get inside the cottage. And I haven't any tea.'

'In that case, I think I'll bring my own,' announced Greg, calmly disposing of her objections. 'And a few basic supplies to see you through the night.'

Before she could protest, he swung himself down into the cabin and reappeared a couple of minutes later with a knobbly looking old khaki rucksack slung over one shoulder. 'Now, let's get you into the dinghy and we'll go ashore,' he said.

It was rather unnerving to scramble down into a heaving dinghy in a straight skirt, but with Greg's assistance Rose managed it somehow. Instructing her to sit down in the stern, he fitted the rowlocks into their holes and shipped the oars. Then he untied the painter and, crouching low, took his place in the centre seat facing her. With a deft movement he unshipped the oars and began to row. His powerful arms sent the tiny craft skimming effortlessly across the water, but as they neared the band of white foam where the waves were breaking on the beach, a fresh difficulty presented itself to Rose.

'How do we get ashore?' she asked, glancing uneasily down at her best navy leather shoes. 'Do we just jump into the waves and walk?'

'I do,' agreed Greg with an unholy glint in his eyes. 'You jump into my arms and let me carry you. And no arguments, my dear.'

Rose opened her mouth to protest and then closed it again. Obviously it was the only sensible thing to do. All the same, she wasn't looking forward to it one bit, or, if she was, she didn't intend to admit it even to herself. There was a sudden, exhilarating surge and they found themselves carried forward on the crest of a wave to ground on the soft sand amid a seething rush of foam. Greg jumped out, wearing his knee-high rubber fisherman's boots, reached into the bow of the dinghy for a small anchor which he dug into the sand, then turned to Rose with a look of sly anticipation on his face.

'Come on, then,' he ordered as he held out his arms to her. 'What are you waiting for?' With as much dignity as she could muster, Rose crept gingerly towards him, then suddenly felt herself swept off her feet and into his arms. In spite of her resolution to remain calm, her body stiffened at his touch and she looked up at him with a flash of alarm. There was still amusement and warmth in his eyes, but there was also something else, a look of hungry, primitive desire that made her blood pause and then throb hotly and violently through her veins. For a moment their eyes met in wordless understanding and she could feel the tumultuous thudding of his heart beneath the thin fabric of his shirt, then he muttered something unintelligible under his breath and began to stride fiercely towards the beach.

A moment later Rose was on her feet on the white sand, although she felt oddly unsteady on her legs. Glancing back, she saw that Greg had returned to the water's edge and was hauling the dinghy up on the sand, out of the reach of waves. She could see the lines of strain in his body as he half carried, half dragged it across the sand, and could not suppress a twinge of admiration at his strength. Then she gritted her teeth in annoyance. She must stop behaving like some ridiculous teenager! It was absurd, undignified. Deliberately turning her back on Greg, she swung round to face the emerald-green landscape that rose in front of her, so much more vividly green than anything she had ever seen in Australia. She was still gazing at it, drinking in its unfamiliar beauty, when Greg appeared beside her and put one arm casually around her shoulders.

'That's your aunt Em's cottage up there on the right,' he said, pointing to a gabled roof barely visible above a hawthorn hedge about two hundred yards away. 'Your new home, Rose.'

A shiver went through her as much at the pressure of his fingers on her shoulder as at the words he had spoken. Her new home, yes. But would she find happiness here?

CHAPTER TWO

FIVE minutes later Rose stood outside the front gate of the cottage and took a long breath of pure delight.

'Isn't it beautiful?' she demanded.

Greg's eyebrows rose sceptically as he took a long, hard look at the gabled roof, which was encrusted with yellow lichen and had several of its slate tiles missing, at the peeling pink paint on the walls, at a broken pane of glass in one of the front windows, at the weathered grey wooden outhouses that leaned drunkenly away from the sea breezes.

'I don't know,' he said in a troubled voice. 'It looks as if it needs a fair bit of work done on it to me.'

'Oh, men!' retorted Rose scathingly, and pushed open the gate, which promptly broke loose from one of its hinges and dangled askew.

Greg gave an explosive chuckle which he hastily turned into a cough when she glared at him. Rose tossed her head defiantly. All right, maybe the cottage did need a bit of work, but she wasn't afraid of getting busy with a scrubbing brush and some paint. And nothing could spoil the perfection of the garden even if it did look wild and unkempt. On the sunny side of the garden a variety of shrub roses rioted in colourful profusion, filling the air with their sweet perfume, while in a shady nook between the house and the hawthorn hedge a sea of vivid blue hydrangeas tossed in the breeze. A candy-pink clematis had run riot over the outhouses and was now trying vigorously to climb the drainpipe at the side of the house, while purple buddleia bushes near the front

25

gate provided a haven for swarms of butterflies. Every
other available nook and cranny was filled with summer
annuals, poppies and columbines and striped petunias.
What did it matter if the lawn was now knee-high and
rank with weeds, or if the paving on the path was chipped
and overgrown with dandelions? These things could all
be fixed by someone with plenty of energy and a good
set of gardening tools. Yet even Rose's optimistic spirit
sank a little when she saw how the guttering was sagging
over the front porch and the steps were broken and
leaning to one side. Wouldn't repairs like that be
expensive?

'Look, the cottage is named after you,' joked Greg,
pointing to the sign over the door. 'Rose Cottage, 1742.'

'Actually, it's the other way round,' Rose corrected
him. 'I'm named after the cottage. But don't let's hang
about. I can't wait to see inside.'

Unfortunately, when she inserted her key into the front
door, she found that it would not budge. She looked
helplessly at Greg.

'The wood is probably swollen from the rain,' he said
with a shrug. 'Or else your aunt Em didn't use the front
door much. I could force it open for you, but why don't
we try the back door first?'

The back door was more co-operative but the results
were hardly encouraging. When it finally creaked open
they found themselves in a dim back porch with a strong
smell of rising damp and the sound of a tap dripping
persistently somewhere near by. As Rose's eyes became
accustomed to the gloom, she saw that the wallpaper
was stained and discoloured and that some of the floor-
boards were rotting beneath their feet. The first, faint
misgivings began to stir inside her. All the same, she
wasn't prepared to give up without a fight.

'Let's take a look at the rest of the house,' she said
bracingly. 'I'm sure it'll be much better.'

It wasn't. If anything, it was worse. The discovery of her suitcases in the front bedroom and a few basic food items with a friendly note from her neighbour cheered her up briefly, but her enthusiasm was soon quenched as she explored further. All the four downstairs rooms were spacious and charmingly old-fashioned with carved wooden fireplaces and small paned windows, but there were patches of damp on the walls and the only floor covering was a faded pink carpet square in the front bedroom. Most of the furniture was old and shabby without being antique, and the only indoor plumbing appeared to be a tap in the kitchen sink and a claw-footed bath with rusty legs. The upstairs rooms were no better. The stairs themselves had handsome barley-twist newels, but the treads were narrow and worn almost paper-thin in the centre and, judging by the thick layer of dust that covered everything on the first floor, it was probably years since Aunt Em had ever climbed up them. The attics were in the saddest condition of all, crammed full of boxes of old junk and with a couple of big holes in the plaster where rain had come in through missing tiles on the roof. By now, Rose's initial euphoria had completely vanished and she could not help heaving a deep sigh as she followed Greg back down the precarious staircase. As they reached the bottom he turned back and raised his eyebrows at the sight of her woebegone face.

'I think it's time we had that cup of tea,' he said.

Trying to prepare the cup of tea was the final straw for Rose, since the kitchen seemed to be circa 1742 just like the rest of the house. The only cooking equipment was a malevolent-looking rusty black wood stove set into the fireplace and an array of smoke-blackened old teapots and frying-pans. All very well if you wanted to be picturesque, but not much use if you were hungry and thirsty! And the cold tap that was still trickling dis-

mally had left a trail of rusty stains on the enamel sink.
Rose sat down at the scrubbed pine table, buried her
head in her hands and groaned.

'It's hopeless,' she said despairingly. 'I'll never be able
to get it all repaired.'

'Don't talk so foolish,' urged Greg. He grabbed one
of the old kitchen chairs and sat astride it, facing the
wrong way with his chin resting on his folded arms and
a stern look in his eyes. 'You're not going to give up at
the first minor difficulty, are you? You don't have the
look of a coward, my dear.'

A hot surge of rage flooded through Rose's entire body
at this criticism. A moment before she had felt like
bursting into tears. Now she felt like hitting Greg, which
was a definite improvement, but still rather startling. She
had always thought she was a peace-loving person.

'Minor difficulty?' she snorted, gesturing at the chaos
around them. 'I wouldn't call this mess exactly minor.'

Greg shrugged dismissively and his jaw set in an ob-
stinate line. 'It all looks structurally sound to me and
there b'ain't much wrong with it that fifteen thousand
pounds or so wouldn't fix.'

Rose gave a gasp of bitter laughter. 'Fifteen thousand
pounds! You just don't understand! I haven't got nearly
that much money to spare. There was a small legacy that
came with the house, but nothing like that amount. Oh,
Greg! I've come all this way just for an impractical
dream. There's no way I'll ever be able to afford to stay
here.'

Greg's dark eyes took on a keen, brooding expression
as if he was giving the problem his full attention.

'You could take out a bank loan,' he suggested. 'All
you have to do is decide you want this cottage badly
enough and you'll find a way of keeping it.'

'No bank manager in his right mind would lend money to me now,' retorted Rose coldly. 'I'm officially unemployed.'

'Well, don't give up too soon. Let's make a cup of tea.'

'How?' demanded Rose. 'There isn't even any way of boiling water, as far as I can see, unless we fire up that wood stove.'

'Yes, there is,' said Greg. 'There's a gas ring over in that far corner.'

Rose was too disheartened to do anything at first, but when Greg produced coffee, teabags, tinned milk and a box of matches from his knapsack, she roused herself sufficiently to go and find some cups in the old wooden dresser against the wall. Once she had a steaming mug of hot, sweet tea and a digestive biscuit inside her, she found that she felt much better, but all their discussion produced no useful solutions. When they had washed the cups under the dripping tap, Greg moved purposefully towards the door.

'Are you leaving now?' asked Rose, her heart sinking. Greg's glib certainty that she could find a way of restoring the cottage infuriated her. And yet she knew with a sudden twinge of dismay that she did not want him to go.

'Not unless you want me to. I thought I'd try and find some gardening tools out in the shed and cut back a bit of that creeper over the sitting-room window. This place would look much more cheerful with a bit of sunlight in it.'

'There's no need——' began Rose, but he had already gone.

She caught him up in one of the dilapidated old sheds, busily engaged in dusting cobwebs off some rusty garden tools. He handed her a pair of threadbare gloves and an old set of clippers.

'Come on,' he said. 'Let's get to work.'

Rose looked at her watch and was surprised to find that it was now after nine o'clock, but although the sun had set, a pure apple-green twilight still lingered around the hills so that it was perfectly possible to go on working. Back home in tropical Brisbane it would have been dark by six o'clock even in the summer. As they worked it began to grow cooler. An occasional quite strong gust of wind came in from the sea. Rose took out her disappointment about the cottage and her antagonism towards Greg on the Virginia creeper and hacked viciously at the encroaching strands. At last, when the sitting-room window was quite clear and there was a large pile of green creeper clippings underneath it, Greg called a halt. Another sharp gust of wind blew in from the sea and Rose shivered involuntarily.

'Are you cold?' he asked. 'I can light a fire, if you like.'

Rose gave him a shamefaced smile.

'It's just my thin, tropical blood,' she explained. 'I'm not used to a place where it gets cool in the evenings.'

'Well, I'll just get the fire going for you before I go,' he offered.

She followed him back towards the woodpile that was stacked neatly at the rear of the house. A sudden unwelcome thought flashed through her mind.

'Don't you have a wife or a girlfriend you have to get back to?' she asked.

He picked up an axe and began to split some kindling, producing half a dozen neat, dry sticks before he answered. Then he wiped the sweat off the back of his forehead with his hand.

'No,' he replied in a mocking voice. 'I'm a completely unloved man.'

I find that hard to believe, thought Rose as she followed him inside. With those devastating good looks, the sensual, throaty voice and his aura of lazy, animal magnetism, Greg must have women swarming around him all the time. With a sudden miserable sense of self-doubt, she wondered why he was wasting time on her when she was so unmistakably ordinary. She was startled when he suddenly stretched out his hand to her.

'Matches,' he ordered.

She blushed in sudden comprehension as she saw the neat pile of kindling and crumpled newspaper which he had arranged in the fireplace. Hurrying into the kitchen, she retrieved the box of matches and Greg soon had a bright orange blaze crackling in the fireplace.

'Are you hungry?' he asked abruptly. 'I'm starving.'

'There were some tins in the kitchen cupboard——' she began, but he overrode her.

'I can do better than that. I brought a few supplies ashore from the boat. Do you fancy some fried lemon sole?'

He did not wait for the fire to burn down but cooked the fish in an old frying-pan over the gas ring. Half an hour later, replete with delicious fish and a butterscotch pudding from one of the tins in the kitchen followed by a fresh pot of tea, they were both sitting on the lumpy sofa in front of a roaring blaze in the sitting-room. Rose's feelings were in turmoil about Greg's willingness to linger. She had grave suspicions about his motives and she was still smarting from his earlier comments on her cowardice, yet she was sneakingly grateful for his company. At eleven o'clock, when Greg still showed no signs of heading for home, she was just beginning to wonder whether she should raise the subject delicately when a sudden spatter of raindrops hit the window outside.

'Looks as though we're in for some dirty weather,' said Greg, his brows drawing together. 'It'll be a chancy business sailing home in this.'

Rose got to her feet and walked across to the window. Outside it was almost dark and a strong wind was beginning to moan through the trees in the garden. Another spatter of raindrops hit the glass, bringing with them a rush of cool, scented air. It would certainly be a difficult task to get into the dinghy and row out to the yacht in total darkness. But if Greg was a fisherman, surely he was used to that sort of thing?

'These be very dangerous coasts,' he said gravely, as if he had read her thoughts. 'I don't mind going now if you want me to, but I reckon there'll be some powerful bad weather tonight and there's rocks out there that would tear the bottom out of the boat in the darkness.' Rose shivered and looked at him uneasily. How would she feel if he really was shipwrecked all because she had sent him out into the darkness after doing a favour for her?

'I suppose you could stay here,' she said uncertainly.

'That's very kind of you, my love,' said Greg, a shade too quickly. 'Very neighbourly. Thanks very much, I'll be glad to.'

Rose shot him a suspicious look. 'I hope you don't think...' she began. 'What I mean is...I don't...'

Greg looked shocked. 'Of course not,' he replied in a voice full of injured innocence. 'I never thought of such a thing.'

Rose retreated to the sitting-room door. 'Would you like some coffee or something?' she asked to cover her embarrassment.

'That'd be nice,' he agreed. 'And there's a packet of chocolate fudge in my knapsack.'

The evening was taking on a decidedly domestic quality, Rose decided a few minutes later as they sat drinking coffee and chewing delicious chocolate fudge. The sofa had proved too uncomfortable to endure any longer and Greg had suggested that they should sit on the sheepskin rug which he had found bundled in one of the cupboards under the stairs and brought into the sitting-room. Lounging back in its tickly warmth with the flames crackling in the fireplace and the rain drumming at the uncurtained window felt remarkably cosy, so why did she have this sense of mounting tension? She darted a swift sideways look at Greg, but he simply smiled blandly at her and took another gulp of his coffee.

'You said earlier that you were named after the cottage,' he reminded her. 'What did you mean?'

'Exactly that,' she replied. 'My mother grew up here, you see, and she was always terribly fond of the place. Her parents died in the bombing of Plymouth when she was only two years old during World War Two, and Aunt Em, who was her mother's older sister, brought her up. Mum always used to talk about Rose Cottage as if it were heaven and I think calling me Rose was the highest compliment she could possibly pay me.'

Greg nodded thoughtfully. 'You say she loved this place and yet she went to Australia. Why was that?' he asked.

Rose sighed. 'Well, my father was an Australian who was over here on a working holiday. She met him when she was only twenty, fell in love, ran off and married him.'

'And the marriage wasn't happy?' guessed Greg shrewdly.

'How did you know?' demanded Rose. 'Are you clairvoyant or something?'

Greg shook his head, but in the firelight his dark eyes seemed so piercing that she had the uncanny feeling that they could look right into her soul.

'No,' he said. 'But you have a very expressive face and the way you sighed told me a lot. So what happened?'

Rose shrugged. 'Other women. A drinking problem. She divorced him when I was eight years old.'

'But she didn't ever think of coming back to Britain?'

'No. It was sad really. I think she would have given her eye-teeth to come back, but she'd quarrelled with Aunt Em about it in the first place because Em didn't approve of my father and Mum didn't want to admit that she'd been in the wrong. The other thing was that she didn't want to be a burden to Aunt Em. After all, she had three kids and no real training for a job. Besides, Daniel was in high school and didn't want to move and Jane was eleven and perfectly happy in Australia.'

'So what did your mother do? How did she support you? Or did your father do that?'

'No, he didn't,' said Rose bitterly. 'He paid maintenance irregularly for about two years and then vanished. Later we heard that he was working in a mining camp in Western Australia, but I haven't seen him since I was ten years old and I don't want to. Mum went out to work as a cleaning lady for other people. So there you are, then, the story of my life.'

'Not quite,' replied Greg, rising to his feet to put another log on the fire. It went in with a crash, sending a hissing cloud of orange sparks up the chimney. 'You haven't told me much about yourself. What sort of job you had before you came here, what things you enjoy, who you first fell in love with and why.'

'I'd rather not remember who I first fell in love with and why,' said Rose in a hard voice. 'But the rest is easy. My hobbies are reading, gardening and cooking and I have a degree in computer programming. That was my mother's influence, I suppose. She thought it would be a steady, well-paid job, which it was. But I didn't realise that it would also be pretty soul-destroying or that I'd come into contact with some quite nasty people.'

There was no mistaking the vehemence in her tone. All the same, Rose was startled when Greg squatted down beside her, took her hands and pulled her to her feet.

'Who was he, Rose?' he asked bluntly.

'Who was who?' faltered Rose.

'Don't play games with me. The man who hurt you.'

A convulsive spasm passed over her face. 'How did you know?' she asked hoarsely.

His warm hands gripped her shoulders, moving, caressing, stroking away the pain. 'People don't get as upset as that just because they hate jobs,' he said. 'They only look that way if they've been in love and been betrayed. Who was he?'

'My boss,' muttered Rose. 'Martin Inglis.'

'Were you lovers?'

Rose hesitated. 'Yes,' she admitted at last.

'What was he like?' asked Greg with a frown. 'What kind of person?'

She let out her breath in a long sigh. 'I hardly know how to describe him. I was only twenty-two when I first met him and didn't like him much at first. Oh, he was certainly good-looking, in an outdoor sort of way. Big, blond, muscular, rather brash. And very masculine, but the kind of man who doesn't really think much of women except in bed or in the kitchen. He liked horse-racing and flashy sports cars and all-night parties.'

'Doesn't sound much like your type,' observed Greg.

'No, that's right,' agreed Rose unhappily. 'And he always used to tease me about being prim and proper and joke about how I was probably dynamite underneath. Then, after I'd been with the company for a couple of years, we happened to be at a conference at Magnetic Island. I bumped into him on the beach in the moonlight one night and he came straight out and told me that he'd always thought I was gorgeous. I was stunned, but I began to think I'd misjudged him. He didn't kiss me or anything, just looked at me... After we got back to Brisbane, he asked me to have dinner with him. We went out together for a year or so, then he told me he loved me and we...started sleeping together. I always thought marriage would follow but we went on like that for over two years. Then a couple of months ago he suddenly announced his engagement to someone else. I didn't even know about it until I saw it in the newspaper.'

If she had hoped for some sign of outrage or sympathy from Greg, Rose was disappointed. His face was an inscrutable mask, as impartial as that of a judge interested only in the facts.

'Did you have a quarrel or something?'

'No.' Rose's throat hurt as she answered. 'It came completely out of the blue. Of course, I went to his office and demanded an explanation. He said...he said...that he thought I'd understand his position. He was wealthy and successful and people like that couldn't afford to marry beneath them. His fiancée, Delia, came from an important family, but he said I shouldn't be hurt because he wasn't in love with her and there was no need for anything to change in our relationship.'

'So what did you say to that?' demanded Greg.

Rose gave a brief, bitter laugh. 'I told him to drop dead, then I handed in my resignation. As it happened, Aunt Em had just died and left this cottage with a life interest to my mother and the remainder to me. I could see my mother couldn't wait to return to England, but she tried hard to persuade me to get another job in Australia. Except that for once I was fed up with being sensible, so I decided to burn my bridges and come with her. And here I am.'

'Good for you,' said Greg. 'You did the right thing.'

'Did I?' demanded Rose, gesturing at the shabby room that surrounded them. 'Now I'm not so sure. I almost wish I'd stayed in Brisbane.'

'You're not still in love with him, are you?' demanded Greg in a hard voice.

'I don't know!' Rose burst out. 'Love isn't reasonable, is it? Sometimes I think I am, but other times I hate him. Mostly I just feel humiliated and angry to think what a credulous fool I was. How could I have been so easily deceived? And it makes me feel a lot of pain and anxiety too. I don't feel as if I can ever trust another man again. Especially a rich one.'

'That's ridiculous!' said Greg sharply. 'Just because one man disappointed you, that's no reason to think you can never get involved with another one.'

To her astonishment, he suddenly hauled her hard against him, tilted her chin and planted a long, thrilling kiss on her lips. Rose felt shaken and exhilarated and for one crazy, impetuous moment she kissed him back with equal fervour. The firelight flared orange through her closed eyelids, yet its heat seemed to blaze not only on her skin, but also in the innermost depths of her body. As Greg's powerful arms tightened about her, she felt an urgent, pulsating need that made her sway dizzily against him. Her lips parted, trembling, and she offered herself to him with a wanton intensity that both thrilled and shocked her. She heard him utter a low groan deep in his throat and that brought her back to her senses. Aghast at what she had done, she broke away and retreated to the door.

'Look, let's forget that that ever happened,' she said in a strained voice. 'I'm going to bed. Goodnight.'

And in case there should be any misunderstandings, once she had gained the sanctuary of her bedroom, she turned the lock firmly in the door.

* * *

Rose woke early the following morning, roused by the flood of sunlight spilling in through the uncurtained window. For a moment she lay baffled, trying to work out where she was. Then comprehension came jolting back and with it the memory of the previous night. Uttering a low groan, Rose burrowed into the feather pillows and pulled the quilt over her head. Her cheeks went hot with embarrassment as she wondered how she could have been such a fool. She hardly even knew Greg Trelawney, so how could she possibly have kissed him with such abandon? The whole incident was completely unlike her! She had always been calm, sensible, reserved, so how on earth had it happened? She felt angry with herself and angry with Greg too, but here there was a strange confusion in her feelings. He shouldn't have kissed her and yet ... if she was honest with herself, she had to admit that she had enjoyed it. And, even if he hadn't condemned Martin's behaviour, she couldn't believe that Greg himself would ever do anything so cruel. He was too direct, too primitive, too natural for the sort of calculation and subterfuge that came so readily to men like Martin. And was it really so dreadful if Greg had felt powerfully attracted to Rose and simply seized her and kissed her? It wasn't as though he had a wife or girlfriend; he had told her that himself. Deep down she felt certain he was the kind of man she could trust completely. Of course, it mustn't happen again, she must make that quite clear to him, but perhaps there was no need to end their budding friendship...

Five minutes later, dressed in furry slippers and a full-length towelling dressing-gown that covered her cotton nightdress, Rose padded warily into the kitchen. Greg was already dressed and busy boiling the kettle on the gas ring, but he turned to smile at her.

Although he was wearing the same faded jeans and checked red flannel shirt as on the previous day, there was something subtly different about his appearance. Something that nagged at the back of Rose's mind that she could not quite identify... His dark eyes glinted at the sight of her and he seemed completely unperturbed by what had happened the previous night. In spite of his rather mocking smile, he made no attempt to touch her, so why did she feel as uneasy as if she had just stepped into a cage with a drowsing panther?

'Good morning,' said Rose coolly, retreating a pace or two.

'Good morning,' replied Greg with an undertone of amusement in his voice. 'I've got the water-heater going, so once you've been out the back you can have a bath, if you like.'

'Thanks,' said Rose.

After braving the outside loo, which was dark, full of spiders and definitely leaned to one side, Rose was relieved to find the old claw-footed bath brimming with hot water.

'Take your time,' advised Greg. 'I'll make some coffee and toast when you've finished. Pity we haven't got any eggs and bacon.'

But that was a deficiency which was soon to be remedied. Rose had just finished dressing in her severest office suit, which was navy blue with a white pinstripe and made her feel more in control of the situation, when she heard the unmistakable sound of voices from the kitchen. Surprised and curious, she hurried out and found herself warmly embraced by a grey-haired woman of about sixty.

'You must be Rose Ashley,' said the newcomer. 'I'm your neighbour, Joan Penwithick. I was expecting you on the bus yesterday afternoon but you didn't arrive, so when I saw the smoke from the chimney this morning I thought I'd pop down and investigate.'

Joan's brown eyes darted piercingly sideways at Greg as she said this. Rose flushed and launched into a hasty explanation about her lost pocketbook, the missed bus and the sailing trip back from Polperro.

'And, of course, the weather was so bad last night that Greg didn't think it was safe to sail back home, so he stayed here,' she finished lamely.

Joan snorted. 'Didn't seem that bad to me,' she pronounced. 'I've seen you out in far worse gales than that, Greg Trelawney. Anyway, why couldn't you just sleep aboard your yacht in the bay?'

For once Greg looked completely disconcerted, but instead of answering, he strode forward and grabbed the string bag that was dangling from Joan's right hand.

'Well, what have you got here?' he asked. 'Bacon and eggs? Oh, you're a fine woman, Joan, my love. Why don't you sit down and ask Rose all about her mother while I fry these up?'

Successfully diverted, Joan took her place at the kitchen table opposite Rose and fired an eager volley of questions about Fay Ashley, who was only five years her junior and whom she had known in their schooldays. A complicated recital of the Ashley family history ensued, followed by an equally complicated account of the Penwithick saga, complete with the news that Joan's second grandchild was due any day now. When she paused for breath, Greg set sizzling plates of bacon and eggs and mugs of hot coffee in front of both of them. Then he sat down to tackle his own hearty breakfast, but he had scarcely swallowed his first forkful of bacon when Joan went on the attack again.

'Why aren't you at the shipyard in Plymouth, Greg?' she demanded. 'Surely things are too busy for you to have a holiday on a Tuesday?'

Greg hastily swallowed a mouthful of bacon and scowled at Joan. 'I reckon they can do without me once

DARK PIRATE   41

in a while,' he replied, his Cornish accent suddenly stronger than ever.

'Shipyard?' echoed Rose. 'What shipyard? Oh, Greg, you haven't missed a day's work just so that you could help me? What if you get fired?'

It was Joan's turn to choke on a mouthful of bacon, and Greg slapped her vigorously on the back.

'Well, I don't want to rush you, Joan,' he said. 'But if you've finished your breakfast, I think you'll have to excuse Rose and me. We've got an appointment with the bank manager in Looe this morning.'

'Have we?' asked Rose incredulously, after Greg had seen Joan off the premises.

'We soon will have,' promised Greg. 'Hugh's an old friend of mine and I know he'll help us out. I'll just go up to the phone box at the corner and give him a ring.'

Feeling as helpless as if she were being swept along by some roaring river in full flood, Rose soon found herself shepherded out of the door and on to a bus for Looe.

'What about your boat?' she objected as they bowled away between the leafy hawthorn hedges.

'I'll come back and fetch it later,' said Greg. 'First we've got to get you a loan to fix up the cottage.'

'This is ridiculous,' protested Rose. 'Look, Greg, I'm unemployed, except for a bit of freelance programming which I'm finishing off for Inglis's—I was part-way through it when I left and the systems manager begged me to complete it on a contract basis. He'd always been helpful to me, so I agreed. But once that's finished, I'll have no income at all. I'll never get a loan for the cottage. Never, never!'

But she was wrong. Greg might be only a simple fisherman, but he seemed to have remarkably good contacts. When they entered the bank building in East Looe, there was an unmistakable deference in the manner of the staff as they spoke to him. What was more, the manager Hugh Thomas, a short, grey-haired man of about sixty with a cautious expression, treated both of them as if they were royalty.

'I'll come back for you in half an hour,' promised Greg. 'You should have everything arranged by then, shouldn't you?'

'Yes, yes, of course,' agreed Hugh, glancing down at Rose and sighing. 'Now, Miss Ashley, if you could just step into my office and give me a few details...'

Rose had a dreamlike sense of unreality throughout the interview that followed. After all, she didn't even have a passport as proof of her identity, let alone a proper job or any sign of financial stability apart from the title deeds of Aunt Em's cottage, which were lodged with a local solicitor. And yet Hugh Thomas seemed extra-ordinarily unfazed by all of this and very soon produced a document for her to sign with terms of interest that seemed to her inexperienced eye remarkably favourable. When Greg arrived after the prescribed half-hour she stumbled out, looking dazed.

'Well?' he demanded. 'How did it go?'

'He's agreed,' she said in disbelief. 'A fifteen-thousand-pound personal loan and another five-thousand-pound overdraft facility. And he's supplied me with some cash for immediate expenses. I can't believe it!'

'Oh, Hugh's a pretty shrewd man,' said Greg. 'He knows a good business proposition when he sees one. And a trustworthy client. Come on, let's go and have a cream tea to celebrate.'

He took her to an unpretentious tea-shop down by the waterfront and they sat outside on a balcony gay with red geraniums and striped blue and white umbrellas.

'It's going to be quite a long time before that cottage is fit to take in paying guests,' worried Rose aloud. 'I'll have to buy a PC with an eighty-megabyte hard disk so I can finish this stock-control program. Oh, dear! How am I going to cope?'

'That's easily organised,' said Greg, reaching into his pocket for a battered notebook and Biro. 'Tell me what kind you need and I'll try and get you a suitable machine in Plymouth. Now, the next thing is to organise your renovations. I can put you on to some good tradesmen who'll save you a packet, but there's another suggestion I'd like to make to you.'

'What's that?' asked Rose warily.

'You know what it's like when you're renovating a house. There's always a terrible mess, no electric power, no proper plumbing, dust everywhere. Well, my suggestion is this: while they're fixing up your house, why don't you move into my cottage?'

CHAPTER THREE

'WHAT do you mean?' demanded Rose in an outraged voice. 'Move into your cottage?' Greg tried hard to look like an innocent lamb and failed dismally. Nothing could conceal the disturbing glint in his dark eyes as they moved lingeringly down over her body.

'You're too hard on me, Rose,' he protested. 'You're not afraid I'm going to seduce you, are you?'

'No, I'm not afraid you're going to seduce me!' exclaimed Rose hotly and then hurriedly lowered her voice as she saw several people glance over their shoulders in an interested fashion. 'I wouldn't put it past you to try, but I'm not afraid of it because I wouldn't let it happen!'

'Then what's the problem?' asked Greg.

'The problem is that you lure me into doing things that I don't intend to do and that I regret afterwards, like going to see the bank manager—not that I regretted that afterwards because it all turned out so well,' said Rose, getting rather tangled up. 'Oh, you know perfectly well what I mean, Greg. I don't want to be alone with you!'

'But you wouldn't be,' said Greg. 'I wouldn't be there.'

Rose was conscious of an unexpected stab of disappointment. 'What do you mean, you wouldn't be there?' she demanded, her eyes narrowing suspiciously.

Greg spread a scone with jam and cream, took an appreciative bite and then sipped some tea before he answered. 'I'm based in Plymouth right through the week,' he said. 'I'm only ever here on weekends.'

'Then what were you doing here yesterday and today?' challenged Rose. 'On a Monday and Tuesday?'

Greg sighed and stroked his chin. 'You're very unsportsmanlike to point that out,' he complained. 'Anyway, that was an exception. Most weeks I'm busy at the shipyard Monday to Friday and I only come home on the weekends. You'd have my cottage to yourself nearly all of the time and you'd actually be doing me a favour if you stayed there.'

'Doing you a favour? What do you mean?'

'It would discourage housebreakers if you were staying in the house.'

'Housebreakers? In Polperro?'

'There are purse snatchers,' Greg reminded her.

Rose was silent for a moment, drumming her fingers on the red and white checked tablecloth and then fiddling restlessly with a geranium in a glass vase. She felt an unwelcome stir of interest in Greg's proposition, but events were moving far too fast for her. In the past she had always thought of herself as cautious, sensible, slow to take risks or tackle new relationships. It had been several months before she had even let Martin kiss her, much less talk her into sleeping with him. And she had never really enjoyed it, which only confirmed her dismal certainty that she was more aloof than most women. Yet Greg Trelawney seemed to crash through her reserve without any effort at all. In fact, his brooding dark eyes and crooked smile were beginning to hold an almost hypnotic fascination for her. With a tremulous leap of the heart, she realised exactly what she feared if she went to stay with him. Not Greg. Herself. A fiery, aching sweetness throbbed through her as she remembered how he had kissed her in the firelight. What would she do if he did that again? Order him to stop or...? A shudder thrilled through her body and her eyes flashed up to his in a swift, tormented glance. It was madness even to

think of such things! Madness. No. She liked Greg and
trusted him, but she wasn't going to invite heartbreak a
second time.

'It's impossible——' she began urgently.

'It's sensible,' he cut in. 'Look, Rose, your great-aunt's
house is going to be uninhabitable and you know it. You
haven't got any money to spend on a hotel and my
cottage is standing empty. Why not take advantage of
it? Are you going to let your stupid pride stand in the
way?'

Rose's tempestuous feelings found vent in anger.
'That's a very sneakily worded question,' she snapped.
'If I say yes, it's like admitting that I'm proud and stupid,
and if I say no, I've played right into your hands.'

'*Touché*,' murmured Greg admiringly. 'You're no fool,
are you, Rose?'

'No, I'm not,' she retorted. 'And I'm not going to be
sweet-talked into this. I'm sorry, Greg, I'm genuinely
grateful for all you've done for me, but enough is
enough. I don't want to be so much in your debt. And
anyway, what about the weekends? What would we do
then?'

'We slept together last night,' pointed out Greg.

Several newspapers rustled and there was a discreet
turning of heads on other parts of the balcony.

'No, we did not!' hissed Rose, wishing passionately
that she could manage to shout and whisper at the same
time. 'You slept in the spare room and nothing happened between us!'

'Nothing?' taunted Greg.

Rose's face flamed at the reminder of that kiss in the
firelight. She tossed her head angrily and her blue eyes
shot sparks.

'I'm sorry,' she said in a tense, rapid voice. 'But I am
not going to come and live in your cottage.'

Greg sighed and shook his head. 'That's a pity,' he said soberly, looking straight into her eyes. 'I didn't think you really cared about convention. When I first saw you, I thought to myself, Now there's a woman who looks conventional, but isn't. She's just on the brink of discovering who she is and she's got the courage to find out. Well, it seems I was wrong.'

Rose flinched at the unmistakable sarcasm in his voice, then she glanced around the balcony and noticed how the other customers' eyes shifted hastily away from her. Her eyes came back to Greg's with a proud, defiant expression. In that instant she reached a hard decision. She knew he was intentionally goading her, but there was enough truth in his words to touch her on the raw. Was she always going to hang back from challenges or was she going to find out what she really wanted from life?

'You're not going to give up at the first sign of difficulty, are you?' she demanded in a deliberate echo of his words the previous day. 'You don't have the look of a coward, my dear.'

A gleam of admiration illuminated Greg's face. He reached across and gripped her hand so hard that it hurt.

'Let's go home,' he urged hoarsely.

Greg's cottage was as spacious as Aunt Em's, but in far better condition. It stood high on the cliff-top just to the west of Polperro, with a dry-stone wall around it, a ship's wheel set in its sparkling teal-blue gate, a garden full of lavender and roses in the front and a paved terrace and dazzling view of the ocean in the rear. He led her round to the back of the house and opened an unlocked glass door which led into a Victorian-style conservatory.

'I see you take special precautions against housebreakers,' commented Rose drily.

'You're a sharp-tongued woman, Rose Ashley,' protested Greg. 'There's nothing really worth stealing here anyway.'

This wasn't strictly true. Although old, the cottage had been lovingly restored with an emphasis on marine antiques. Rose felt certain that some of the barometers, brass compasses, old-fashioned telescopes and intricately decorated scrimshaw in glass-fronted cabinets must be valuable collectors items. Yet it was true that apart from these objects the cottage was simple to the point of bareness. Oh, there were a few modern comforts. Two well-appointed bathrooms, one upstairs, one downstairs with a lot of dark wood panelling, glass fittings and superb views over the sea, and a kitchen which looked pure eighteenth century but had a modern refrigerator, freezer and electric mixer tucked away behind carved wooden doors. The furniture was comfortable too, with brass beds, an old cedar dining suite and carved oak settles discreetly complemented by inner spring mattresses and deep, soft leather couches in the conservatory. All the same, several of the adjuncts normally considered essential to modern living were notably absent. There was no television, no telephone, no dishwasher.

'You must find it very quiet here,' marvelled Rose when they returned to the conservatory after a complete tour of the house.

'I do,' agreed Greg. 'That's the whole attraction of the place for me. It's peaceful just the way it was when I was a kid.'

'You grew up here, then?' asked Rose.

Greg nodded reminiscently as he gazed out over the brick terrace and the drifts of blue hydrangeas to the hedge that marked the back boundary and, beyond that, the ocean.

'Yes,' he replied. 'Although I only ever came home to eat and sleep. In the daytime I ran wild with my brother and sister. Fishing from the coves, collecting frog spawn from the ponds inland, damn near breaking our necks on the cliff path half a dozen times a day. It was an ideal life for a kid.'

'Do your brother and sister still live here?' asked Rose with interest.

Greg shook his head. 'No, they've gone to foreign parts. Paul's an oil man in Scotland and Helen's a nurse in London.'

Rose, who had just travelled twelve thousand miles, hastily swallowed a gulp of laughter at this interesting definition of foreign parts.

'What about your parents?' she asked unsteadily. 'Are they in foreign parts too?'

Greg frowned at her, as if completely baffled by the reason for her amusement. 'My mother is,' he agreed. 'She said she wanted to see a bit more of the world before she was too old to enjoy it. She left two years ago and she spends most of her time on the Atlantic coast. I visit her three or four times a year and she seems happy enough. My father's dead.'

'Oh, I'm sorry.'

'Don't be,' said Greg with a shrug. 'He was seventy-two when it happened and he'd had a good innings. Lived here his entire life in a place that he loved, surrounded by friends, had a good marriage and kids he was proud of, worked at sea until his fingers were too stiff to hold a net and then sat at the end of his garden watching the boats until one night he died peacefully in his sleep. What is there to be sorry about in that?'

'Nothing,' replied Rose, much moved.

'Of course, he didn't make much money,' admitted Greg. 'But he never thought that was important.'

'It isn't!' insisted Rose warmly. 'I think having your friends and family about you and living in a place you love is much, much more important than money. Actually, from what I've seen of money, it really destroys people's values. I'd never want to marry a rich man.'

'Hmm,' said Greg. 'Well, speaking of marriage, take a look at this. It's a photo of my parents on their wedding-day, taken outside the church at Talland. My father's buried there too.'

'Is he?' asked Rose with interest, examining the silver-framed photo of a tall dark-haired man in his mid-thirties and a woman about ten years his junior, both dressed in the style of the early nineteen-fifties. 'That's a coincidence—so are my grandparents. I'd like to go and visit the church some time, if you'll tell me where it is.'

'We can go now, if you like,' suggested Greg. 'It's a nice walk along the cliff path.'

'But don't you have to get back to work?' demanded Rose with a worried frown. 'Aren't you afraid they'll sack you from the shipyard?'

This suggestion appeared to afford Greg considerable amusement. For some reason he looked as if he was trying hard not to laugh, but at last he managed to assume an expression of gravity.

'No, not really,' he said. 'But I suppose I'll have to leave tonight or early tomorrow morning.'

Rose was silent and thoughtful on the walk to Talland. Now that she had made the daring decision to stay with Greg, she was busy trying to justify it to herself. Really, there was no risk, she told herself. Greg might be unusually frank and direct but that didn't necessarily mean that he wanted to have an affair with her. Probably that kiss last night was an impetuous impulse which he regretted as much as she did. If only she could stay cool and pleasant, they might be able to develop a very rewarding friendship based on mutual respect... She wished his hair didn't look quite so thick and glossy about the collar of his shirt. It made her want to run her fingers through it... With a sigh Rose put on a little burst of speed and caught him up.

Greg's cottage was set on the cliff-top about two miles west of Polperro, so that they had a brisk walk along the track which threaded its way between huge, sweet-smelling yellow gorse bushes, through stands of bracken, over neat wooden stiles, plunging down into valleys and up over headlands until it brought them at last to Polperro itself. Rose would rather have liked to linger in the village, but Greg seemed keen to keep going. Before long they had crossed the stream, made their way through the picturesque back alleys with their pre-cipitous flights of steps and were toiling up yet another stretch of the cliff path on their way to Talland.

Rose fell instantly in love with the old stone church set high on the cliff-top. There was a timeless peace about its hushed interior with the sun streaming in through one of the tall windows, lighting up the polished wooden pews and the uneven flagstones on the floor. Hardly daring to breathe, she tiptoed around, inspecting the carved memorials of women long dead with their quaint Elizabethan ruffs and long dresses and tried to imagine the feelings of more recent worshippers. Her mother, as a child fidgeting beside Aunt Em in the unhurried days after World War Two, Greg's parents getting married in front of this very altar, villagers enjoying a few mo-ments' peace at the end of a hectic week...

'Come outside and look at the view from the cliff,' whispered Greg.

Almost reluctantly, Rose followed him outside and paused on the vivid green grass that sloped away to-wards the cliff's edge. Far away on the blue horizon she could see ships so tiny that they appeared almost motionless. Far above her seagulls soared, their wings flashing like gold in the sunlight.

'I envy your parents,' she said dreamily. 'What a wonderful way to start a marriage—to walk out into all of this. If I was ever going to get married I'd want it to be here.'

Greg gave her an odd look but did not comment. To her embarrassment Rose realised that she had been guilty of thinking aloud. She couldn't imagine what had come over her. Somehow Greg's habit of speaking his mind quite openly was rather contagious and she had begun to feel as if she could bare her heart to him, just as if he were an old and dear friend. Normally she would never have dreamed of discussing her feelings about marriage with a man she hardly knew! Yet obviously Greg was taken aback by her frankness. Did he think, horror of horrors, that she had designs on him as a likely candidate? Rose's cheeks burned with embarrassment and she tried hastily to retrieve her dignity.

'Not that I ever intend to get married,' she added in a rush.

'Why not?' demanded Greg.

Rose had only to think of Martin and one excellent reason presented itself. A spasm of disgust crossed her face.

'Why bother?' she countered. 'These days you don't have to be married to have sex, or even children if it comes to that. And I think falling in love is vastly overrated as a reason for getting married.'

Greg frowned and opened his mouth as if he was about to argue with her. Then his expression changed. A tough, cynical smile twisted the edges of his mouth.

'I couldn't agree with you more,' he said curtly. 'Half the time when people imagine they're in love it's nothing but a violent sexual passion that would very soon burn itself out. And if they were fool enough to marry because of it they'd soon find themselves bored and disillusioned with each other.'

Rose felt perversely annoyed by Greg's cynical view of marriage, even though he was only agreeing with her own words. A complex tide of emotions surged through her. Disappointment, bitterness, mistrust. In her experience, whenever men proclaimed their opposition to marriage it usually meant that they wanted all the benefits of it without any of the formalities or commitments.

'So you don't approve of marriage in any shape or form?' she asked coldly.

Greg shrugged. 'I didn't say that. It's all right for some people, I suppose. But it's all this fuss about love that really infuriates me. I think on the whole I'd prefer a straight-out marriage of convenience to all the drama women seem to thrive on. A marriage where you cemented business alliances by taking a bride with no wild expectations of living happily ever after. Although even that has precious little appeal for me.'

'Then you don't think you'll ever marry?' asked Rose, wondering why the question sent such a jag of pain through her.

'I doubt it,' replied Greg with a shrug. 'I suppose I want far too much. My parents had a wonderful marriage, stormy but never anything less than totally passionate and committed, and I'm not prepared to settle for anything less. I'd want a woman who was passionate in bed, but had good sense and stamina in dealing with the problems of life once the first rosy glow had worn off. Someone intelligent, resourceful, adaptable. Not just someone who could set my heart on fire, but a woman who could move between two worlds and be happy and at ease in both. A simple fisherman's wife here and——' He suddenly bit off the words as if he had said more than he had intended.

'And?' prompted Rose.

Greg threw her a surly look and dug his hands into the pockets of his faded jeans. 'Nothing,' he said, hunching his shoulders. 'I got carried away. I don't suppose there's any point telling you this, but there are times when I've thought that I could be more than just a simple fisherman.'

There were undercurrents in his voice that puzzled Rose. Resentment, a black, bitter humour and something else. A hesitant, almost unwilling desire to share something with her. But Rose was not at all sure she wanted to share anything with Greg Trelawney, especially when he looked at her with those dangerously seductive dark eyes. If she let him get close to her she had a disturbing suspicion that they would end up sharing far more than mere confidences. And Rose had no intention of being lured into an affair with Greg, especially when his own admissions had made it clear that it could never lead to anything more. Her voice when she replied was deliberately light and bracing as if she were an agony aunt giving good advice to a man wanting to improve himself.

'I'm sure you could,' she said. 'You're so dynamic that you could have anything you set your heart on.'

Greg's lip curled scornfully at this meaningless babble. 'Don't tempt me,' he said softly. 'I might set my heart on having you.'

Rose was so shaken by the smouldering expression in Greg's eyes that she broke away and walked across to the cliff's edge. Turning back to him, she spoke in a strained voice, making a deliberate attempt to change the subject.

'How did you become a fisherman? Was it just an inevitable result of geography?'

'All right, Rose,' said Greg's deep voice at her elbow. 'If you want to make light conversation and take things slowly, I'm prepared to humour you. Yes, I think it was inevitable. Although not only because of geography. As far back as I can remember, I always loved the sea and big ships.'

'So how did you get started?' asked Rose, deliberately shading her eyes and looking out to sea, so that she would not have to look at the tall, powerful man who stood so disturbingly beside her.

'I left school when I was fifteen, I was apprenticed to a boat builder and I spent the next four years learning the trade. After that, I set out to make my mark on the world.'

The words were spoken with such energy and purpose that Rose almost felt scorched by them. For the first time it struck her as rather odd that Greg, who was so obviously intelligent, dynamic and hell-bent on having his own way, should have been content to remain in a relatively humble occupation in a small village.

'What did you do?' she asked, intrigued.

'Well, the minute I finished my apprenticeship, I set my first goal, which was to buy my own fishing boat before I was twenty-five.'

'And did you?'

'Yes,' he said with pride in his voice. 'You sailed on her yesterday. The *Merastadu*. In fact, I was twenty-two when she came into my hands. She looked a wreck, but she had beautiful, clean lines and I fixed her up and refitted her. Then I leased her out for a while and set off in the North Sea fleet to make some money at fishing.'

'You never felt inclined to stay away?' asked Rose.

He shook his head emphatically. 'Why would I want to stay away from the most beautiful place in the world?' he challenged. 'No, I always vowed I'd come home to Cornwall the minute I could afford it, which I did when I was twenty-five. And I've been fishing and boat building ever since, depending on where the money was.

I only keep the *Merastadu* these days as a pleasure craft, but I could never sell her. She was the first boat I fell in love with and I have a faithful heart.' There was something so taunting, so provocative in the sideways glance that he cast her with these words that Rose felt an unwelcome shiver pass through her body. Did Greg have a faithful heart? With women as well as with boats? And why should it matter to her in any case? Tossing her head, she moved away from him a second time and strode briskly towards the path that led out of the churchyard.

'Speaking of the *Merastadu*,' she said, 'shouldn't we be getting back to her? You can't leave her forever in Pisky Bay, can you?'

Greg sighed and strode after her. 'No, you're right,' he said impatiently. 'We ought to be getting back. There's your luggage to collect too.'

'Yes,' agreed Rose. 'And I must speak to Joan Penwithick. I really ought to tell her what my plans are in case my mother phones her.'

Greg frowned and a thoughtful look came into his eyes. 'Actually, it might be better to avoid that,' he said carelessly. 'If you go into Joan's place, ten to one she'll keep you trapped there, gossiping, and I really am in a bit of a hurry to get away this evening. I'll tell you what, why don't you go to my house and wait for me? I can easily explain to Joan what you're doing, then fetch your suitcases and bring them back on the boat.'

Rose chewed her lip thoughtfully and darted him a swift, assessing glance. Not for the first time in her dealings with Greg, she felt as if she were a particularly stupid and wayward lamb being expertly driven into a pen by an unusually adroit sheepdog. Some deep-seated instinct warned her beyond doubt that Greg was deliberately trying to keep her away from Joan Penwithick. But why should he? The question tingled on her tongue, but she felt sure that if she voiced any doubts he would simply brush them aside with a glib explanation. No, better to wait until he had left and then have a chat to Joan herself. She could always walk to Polperro and find a phone box, and it was only polite to have a few words with Joan herself. In any case, while it might not be strictly ethical, there was a lot more she wanted to know about Greg Trelawney... His eyes met hers, shrewd and piercing, but she smiled innocently back at him.

'All right,' she agreed.

A couple of hours later, when Greg had set out for Pisky Bay, leaving Rose alone in his cottage, she put her plan into action. Shutting the door behind her, she walked back to Polperro and found a public phone box. Joan's telephone rang for so long that Rose almost gave up, but at last it was answered.

'Hello, Joan Penwithick here.' Something in the older woman's voice sounded oddly flustered. 'Who's speaking, please?'

'It's Rose. Rose Ashley. Joan, I——'

'Oh, Rose! What a good thing you phoned when you did! I've got the most wonderful news. My daughter Elizabeth has just had her new baby and I'm simply walking on air. I'm in a dreadful flap because I'm trying to get ready to drive over to Dorset tonight and stay with my older grandchild for a few days. But is there anything I can do for you before I leave?'

Rose hesitated. 'I don't want to delay you now, Joan,' she said. 'I thought I'd better let you know what my plans are. Aunt Em's cottage is practically uninhabitable, I'm afraid, and Greg Trelawney has very kindly offered to let me stay at his house until the repairs are done. I just wanted to let you know in case you wondered where I was.'

There was a pause at the other end of the line, a pause that seemed full of suspicion and disapproval.

'My dear Rose,' said Joan at last. 'I know you're a grown woman and this is really none of my business, but do you think it's wise to stay with Greg? He's a very good-looking man and he has a reputation for getting exactly what he wants, whether it's in business or matters of the heart. He may seem soft-voiced and casual and good-natured, but underneath he's as hard as Cornish granite. I suppose he wouldn't have got on so well in the world, would he, if it were otherwise? But I don't honestly like thinking of an impressionable young woman staying there and that's the truth. You'd be much wiser not to do it.'

Rose was more shaken than she cared to admit by Joan's words, but there was a stubborn streak in her character and she had never liked having other people tell her what to do. In any case, how was she to explain to Greg if she changed her mind now? And where else could she go?

'It's very kind of you, Joan,' she said with more poise than she felt. 'But I can assure you that I'm in no danger of losing my head over Greg. I feel certain this arrangement will work out perfectly well.'

There was an incredulous snort at the other end of the line. 'Well, I hope you're right, my love,' replied Joan dubiously. 'But if it doesn't, you just come and stay at my place. I'll leave the key under the first flowerpot in the potting shed for you. I don't expect I'll be away for more than a week, but you make yourself at home whether I'm there or not.'

Feeling more than a little disturbed by this conversation, Rose muttered a few words of congratulation about the new baby, then said goodbye and replaced the receiver. What exactly had Joan meant? If only she had come right out and told Rose the truth, instead of dropping these mysterious hints, it would have made things much easier. As it was, Rose felt a profound uneasiness, without being sure of the reason for it. Why couldn't Greg be trusted with an impressionable young woman? Was he notorious as the village heartbreaker? And what had Joan meant by referring to the way Greg had 'got on so well'? Of course, owning his own boat was quite an achievement, but surely not enough to justify the undertone of awe in the woman's voice? As she emerged from the telephone booth Rose was so pre-occupied with these tantalising problems that she must have taken a wrong turning somewhere among the maze of back alleys. Instead of heading along the cliff path, she found herself going higher and higher up the western side of the gorge towards the road that led inland. With an exclamation of annoyance, she stopped still and looked about her to try to get her bearings. And then she saw him.

On the opposite side of the gorge, in one of the few alleyways wide enough for driving, a man who could not be anyone but Greg Trelawney was stepping out of the passenger seat of a candy-pink sports car. It was too far away for Rose to see his features clearly, but there was no mistaking the glossy, dark hair, the tall, muscular lines of his body, clad in denim jeans and a red checked shirt, or the lithe, animal grace with which he moved. As Rose stared in bewilderment, he came round to the driver's side of the car, halted as if he was speaking to the blonde girl behind the wheel and then bent forward. To Rose's astonishment, the girl suddenly flung her arms around his neck and pulled him down towards her in a desperate gesture. Rose told herself that she shouldn't watch, that this was obviously something private, yet she stood rooted to the spot in horrified fascination as the man tore himself free of the girl's clinging embrace. He seemed to hurl a few exasperated words at her and then strode away without looking back.

The blonde girl put her hand over her eyes and dropped her head in a movement of such pathos that Rose's heart went out to her. Then she rammed the car into gear, turned it jerkily in the driveway of a cottage and drove away in the direction of the main road. Rose stared after the dark-haired man who had now disappeared down a flight of steps and was only intermittently visible between banks of lavender and brightly painted front doors. For a moment she felt a terrible sense of betrayal, then reason asserted itself. It wasn't Greg, it couldn't possibly be Greg! He had told her he was going over to Pisky Bay to fetch his boat, so how could he be here quarrelling with some blonde girl in Polperro at the same time? It was impossible. It must be just a chance resemblance to some other man, perhaps even a relative of his. Shaking her head, Rose made her way back in the direction she had come and this time managed to find the right path.

She had been at home for nearly two hours before Greg finally returned and even then his arrival took her by surprise. She had been sitting on the back terrace, expecting him to appear along the cliff path, when suddenly she heard the sound of a car drawing up outside the front gate. Thinking it might be somebody to call on Greg, she went back inside the house and almost collided with him in the tiny front hall.

'Oh, goodness, you gave me a fright!' she exclaimed. 'I thought you'd walk back along the cliff path.'

He smiled ruefully and gestured at her two large suitcases, which he had just set down on the floor. 'Too much like hard work with that little load,' he retorted. 'I met a friend down by the harbour and he gave me a ride.'

'Oh, of course!' agreed Rose in confusion. 'I'd forgotten about the suitcases. I'm sorry if they were a nuisance to you.'

Greg shook his head. 'No need to apologise, but we must get a few details straight. Charlie's coming back quite soon to give me a lift to Plymouth and I don't want to keep him waiting. I'll just dash into my room and change my clothes, then we'll sort everything out.'

He vanished into the front bedroom and returned five minutes later looking negligently handsome in jeans, a striped navy and white polo top and leather docksider shoes. The intent, brooding look which had lit his face earlier in the day had disappeared and his manner was brisk and practical. Rose was reminded of an office manager giving orders to his staff as he ticked off his instructions on his lean brown fingers.

'OK. Any emergencies where you need to use a telephone, go to the Vinces' house about a hundred yards along the cliff towards Polperro. Take your pick of the upstairs bedrooms and just use anything you need in the house. There's plenty of food in the fridge and a washing-machine and drier if you want to do any laundry.'

'That's a relief,' said Rose. 'I've got a mountain of really grotty clothes in one of my bags that have been accumulating since I left Australia. By the way, can I do any washing for you while I'm at it?'

Greg hesitated and his eyes darted towards his bedroom door. 'No, don't bother,' he said. 'I'll do it myself next weekend. Now, what else did I need to tell you? Oh, yes. You'll find some drawing paper and pencils in the cupboard in the conservatory. Why don't you try sketching up some plans for what you want done with your cottage while I'm gone?'

'That's a good idea,' agreed Rose. 'I really ought to go over and measure up the place first, though.'

'No need,' said Greg crisply. He reached into the back pocket of his jeans, pulled out a notebook and tore off the top sheet. 'I've written down all the measurements for you already.'

Rose stared down in disbelief at the neatly drawn scale plan in front of her. Every measurement was meticulously noted on it, even the width of fireplaces and the stairwell.

'How on earth did you manage that?' she demanded. 'It seems like hours of work.'

Greg's eyes narrowed with amusement and he picked up a leather bag which he had left lying on the floor and brandished a small tool.

'A laser measuring device,' he explained. 'You just point it at the place you want to measure and it does the rest automatically. A boat builder's best friend.'

'I'm impressed!' marvelled Rose.

'Good,' murmured Greg, and suddenly his efficient manner ebbed away as his eyes met hers. Then he spoke in that husky voice that sent tiny thrills of excitement coursing pleasurably up Rose's spine. 'Are you impressed enough to come to the beach with me on Saturday and perhaps have a meal afterwards?'

Rose looked gravely down at the diagram in her hand, deliberately keeping him waiting, but her eyes danced.

'Yes,' she said at last.

'I'll look forward to it,' promised Greg, touching her cheek.

'So will I,' she said rather breathlessly. And then, not knowing how to cope with the intensity of his gaze, she deliberately changed the subject. 'Did you get a chance to talk to Joan?'

He shook his head. 'No, I didn't even try,' he admitted. 'I knew she'd give me an ear-bashing about luring you off to my house, so I just left a note in her letter box saying that you were staying in Polperro for a while and that you'd phone her next week.'

Rose was amused by the slightly shifty look that flitted over Greg's face as he said this, and she was just about to explain that she had telephoned Joan herself when the doorbell rang. Greg went to open the door and ushered in a young man of about twenty-five, who nodded at Rose and rubbed his hands together, while his bright brown eyes darted restlessly around.

'Rose, this is my friend Charlie Polglaze. Charlie, this is Rose Ashley.'

'Pleased to meet you,' said Charlie. 'Ready to go, eh, Greg?'

'Whenever you are,' agreed Greg.

'Coming out to say goodbye to us, my love?' asked Charlie.

Rose followed them out into the driveway where a battered old estate car with its back full of lobster pots and fishing gear stood waiting. Charlie grimaced humorously at it and then raised his eyebrows at Greg.

'So where's your car?' he demanded. 'In the garage getting serviced?'

Greg nodded impassively. 'Yes, that's the trouble when you have an old bomb,' he agreed. 'You're forever getting work done on it.'

Charlie seemed to find this exquisitely funny for some reason. He pumped Rose's hand vigorously and then climbed into the car, muttering to himself.

'Old bomb...old bomb! Forever getting work done...hur, hur, hur.'

Greg led Rose aside a little way so that they were sheltered from Charlie's gaze by a large purple buddleia bush, then he took her by the shoulders and gazed warmly down into her eyes. For a moment she had the intoxicating sensation that he did not want to let her go.

'You're beautiful,' he said in a low voice. 'Do you know that?'

She shook her head, gazing back at him searchingly to see if he was teasing her. A confusing rush of feelings swept through her. Cynicism, disbelief, a turbulent yearning to trust him. With a faint, twisted smile, she shook her head.

'It's true,' he insisted. 'Beautiful, courageous and far more passionate than you've ever guessed. But I'll show you, Rose. When I come back, I'm going to make you face the truth about yourself whether you like it or not.'

Rose felt as if her whole body was scorching with fever as she walked unsteadily back into the house. She heard the noisy retreat of Charlie's old car down the driveway, and it was with a feeling of relief that she slammed the front door of Greg's cottage behind her. Her heart was thudding violently and she leaned back against the door, her eyes straying sightlessly round the hallway and her breath coming in shallow gulps, as she tried to recover her poise. Greg's words still rang in her ears and she shook her head in torment, trying to free herself of the echo. Was he just spinning her a line? Was this all part of some carefully orchestrated plot to lure her into his bed? Did he do this sort of thing to any woman he found remotely attractive? Or did he really recognise something unique, special, intensely passionate in her, Rose Ashley? She wished he would move more slowly, give her a chance to feel safe with him, yet wasn't that like asking an erupting volcano or a tidal wave to move slowly and let people in its path feel safe? A deep shudder went through her as she realised that Greg was like some tempestuous natural force, incapable of moderation himself and determined not to condone it in her. But could she trust him? Or was he just making a fool of her?

Her wandering gaze alighted suddenly on the door of Greg's bedroom with clothes strewn untidily on the floor. In a desperate attempt to regain her sense of normality, Rose decided she would do a load of washing. She opened her own suitcases and took out her dirty laundry, then picked up Greg's scattered garments and made her way to the tiny utility-room tucked out of sight behind a door leading off the kitchen. As she was dropping the clothes into the washing-machine a sudden pang of uneasiness went through her. But why? What was it nagging at the back of her mind? Something that puzzled her. She looked down at the clothes in search of inspiration but there was nothing there to jog her memory. Nothing in the least bit extraordinary about them. Two pairs of faded jeans, underwear, socks, two red checked shirts, one with a green stripe through the red, the other with a navy stripe. The clothes he had been wearing when she had first met him... Suddenly Rose set down the box of detergent with a gasp of indignation as enlightenment dawned.

'The liar!' she breathed. 'The low-down, scheming, unscrupulous fiend!'

For Rose had suddenly discovered what had been troubling her. When Greg had rowed her ashore from the *Merastadu* he had been wearing jeans and a red checked shirt with a navy stripe. Yet the following morning when she had found him in her kitchen cooking breakfast his shirt had had a green stripe. Which meant that he had brought a change of clothes with him when he had left the yacht...and that meant that he had plotted to spend the night ashore in her cottage right from the very first moment! Obviously he had deliberately hung around pruning the creepers and lighting the fire just waiting for the rain to come down and give him an alibi. And all that talk about dangerous coasts and rocks that would tear the bottom out of a boat in the darkness had been just an attempt to play on her guilt and pity... The devious, unscrupulous wretch! Handling the detergent box as if it were full of gunpowder, Rose shook it viciously over Greg's clothes, slammed down the lid of the washing-machine and turned the knob with a furious twist. She was still seething when she marched back into the hall of the tiny cottage and began mechanically to tidy up. What should she do? Should she leave in protest? But her heart sank at the thought of all that was involved in doing that, at least tonight. It was growing dark outside now and she couldn't face walking down to Polperro by torchlight to find a telephone and call a taxi. Or even, for that matter, walking across to the Vinces' place and trying to explain her position.

What made her most angry was the feeling that she had been taken for a ride and that Greg must have been laughing up his sleeve the whole time at her gullibility. But why had he done it? Why did he want to spend the night with her so urgently that he had deceived her? Presumably because he was attracted to her. Perhaps he had even had the nerve to think she might go to bed with him that very first night. But if he had thought that, why had he stopped short after merely kissing her? Not that she would ever have yielded to him, but he must have seen, must have felt how passionately she was responding to him! Rose gave a low groan at the memory of her own indiscretion. Yet surely the way that he had stopped at her insistence meant that he must care at least something for her feelings? She took a deep breath, trying to calm her unruly responses. She felt angry, yes, but in a way almost flattered by Greg's unscrupulous pursuit of her. And realising that she was flattered made her even more angry! But did any of it really matter? All right, so he had kissed her, but he hadn't gone to bed with her, so no real harm had been done. Had it? Yes, she thought with a fresh spurt of annoyance. Because here I am feeling thoroughly unsettled, sparking with crazy impulses, thinking about him all the time instead of about my work, my cottage, my mother, my missing passport, my new life ... Oh, I wish I'd never met him! As she thought this she gave one of her half-open suitcases an impatient kick. To her surprise, a large brown paper parcel slid out of it on to the floor.

'What in the world...?' she began, picking it up with a puzzled frown. 'This can't be mine.'

Then she looked more closely at the parcel. Scrawled on the front in black Biro in a bold, vigorous hand were the words, 'To Rose. Welcome to Cornwall. Love, Greg.' With a sense of profound misgiving, she tore open the package and looked inside.

'Oh, my goodness,' she breathed, setting the contents down on the hall table with trembling fingers. 'Now why in the world did he do that? And just when I'd decided he was an unscrupulous swine, too!'

A wistful, luminous smile played about the corners of her mouth as she looked down at Greg's present. Neatly folded in front of her were the clothes she had admired in the shop at Polperro. The cream woollen sweater decorated with hand-embroidered flowers in coloured silk. Pink, yellow, green, blue. But mainly blue, a pale, forget-me-not blue which would exactly match the colour of her eyes. And a romantic, swirling, blue muslin skirt to match. Rose's eyes pricked with sudden tears.

'Oh, Greg,' she said softly.

CHAPTER FOUR

THE following morning Rose woke early, feeling full of energy and purpose. The first thing she had to tackle was another really good look at her cottage to see what needed to be done to it. It was a glorious, sunny day, so she spent many hot, energetic hours weeding and clipping back shrubs as well as giving the inside of the cottage a thorough scrub. Obedient to Greg's instructions, she took a sketch-pad and pencil with her and tried to figure out what repairs would be needed, but the results were daunting. With a sinking feeling Rose realised that the entire place would have to be gutted, rewired, replumbed, repainted and probably refurnished.

By late afternoon she was exhausted, and caught a bus back to Greg's cottage. Later, revived by a hot bath and a meal, she walked into Polperro and telephoned her mother in Australia. Luckily, her mother's news was good. She was still in hospital, but recovering well from the operation and hoped to join Rose in England within a month. She was anxious to hear about Rose's first impressions of Cornwall and the cottage. Not wanting to alarm her, Rose did not mention the decrepit state of the building, or the disaster of her missing passport, although she did admit with elaborate casualness that she had met some of the local people.

'You sound so odd,' said her mother. 'Just brimming with excitement. You haven't fallen in love, have you?'

'No,' retorted Rose sharply. 'It's...it's just the sea air!'

Yet when Greg arrived on Friday evening, Rose couldn't help wondering whether her mother's shrewd diagnosis made twelve thousand miles away might not be right. Rose had been in the kitchen putting the finishing touches to a meal and had not heard the car, so his arrival took her by surprise. At the sound of footsteps in the hall she came hurrying out, pulling off an apron and smoothing back her hair, then stopped shyly in the doorway to look at him. He was just as tall and disturbingly magnetic as she remembered and his vibrant presence seemed to fill the whole house. For a moment they stood wordlessly looking at each other and a strange, invisible current of attraction seemed to spark between them. Then Greg's gaze tracked lingeringly down over her body.

'I see you got your present, my love,' he murmured.

Rose flushed and looked down at the embroidered sweater and the soft, clinging folds of the skirt that she was wearing.

'Yes. Thank you,' she said, wondering why she had to sound like such a total fool. 'And it was awfully sweet of you. You shouldn't have done it, Greg. It was far too expensive a present, especially for a stranger.'

He took a step towards her. Two steps. His deft brown hand reached out and tidied a stray strand of hair behind her ear, then brushed a smudge of flour from her cheek.

'Oh, we're hardly strangers now, are we, my dear?' he challenged, and his mouth came down on hers in a featherlight kiss.

It was only a moment that they stood there, but Rose felt her lips tingling and her breath coming in a shallow, fluttering rhythm as if she could not get enough air. She had been a fool to think that she and Greg could be friends—she knew perfectly well that friendship wasn't what he wanted from her. Nor, if she was being honest, what she wanted from him. And yet she seemed powerless to resist the force of attraction that swirled and rose about them as relentlessly as a Cornish high tide. With a faint gasp that might have been protest or dismay, or even reckless exhilaration, she laid her head against his chest and felt his fingers clutch possessively at the silky turbulence of her hair. Then, recovering her common sense with an immense effort, she clutched his shoulder, spun him around and steered him towards the dining-room.

'Dinner's ready,' she said in a failing voice.

They worked their way through a delicious meal of golden crusted fish pie, crisp green salad, fresh strawberries and cream and richly aromatic black coffee without saying a single word of any significance. Yet the looks and smiles that passed between them were charged with a meaning that sent waves of guilty, delicious pleasure rippling through Rose's limbs. How could she keep her mind on anything while Greg gazed at her with those warm, caressing, dark eyes? How could she possibly discuss bathrooms and architects and bricklayers and Cornish fishing villages and sailing trips when her whole body cried out to be in his arms? It was as if two different conversations were going on at the same time. One harmless and mundane, that anyone could have overheard without embarrassment, the other silent, wordless, yet fraught with unbearable sexual tension. A silent dialogue of body language that made Rose feel as exhilarated and apprehensive as if she were about to take a parachute jump for the first time. At ten o'clock, unable to bear any more of it, she stammered a disjointed goodnight and headed for the stairs.

Greg caught her up when she was already standing on the bottom step. His hand closed over her wrist as she clutched the banister. 'Don't forget our trip to Talland Bay tomorrow,' he reminded her.

Neither of them bothered to rise early the following morning, and when Rose finally did surface she found that Greg was in the midst of cooking an impressive breakfast featuring orange juice, scrambled eggs, sausages, bacon, grilled tomatoes and enough toast and marmalade to feed the crew of a troop ship. He cast her a long, brooding glance as she entered the kitchen and she felt a tingle of warmth deep inside her as she defiantly returned his gaze. Without taking his eyes off her, he reached for the coffee grinder on the bench beside him.

'You could make the coffee,' he suggested abruptly.

His fingers brushed against hers as he handed her the heavy wood and chrome appliance, and his face was so close that she could easily have stood on tiptoe and kissed his cheek. There was something deeply disturbing about the intimacy of the situation, so it was probably fortunate that a strong smell of sizzling egg white assaulted their nostrils at that moment. 'Something's burning,' Rose warned.

Greg swore under his breath and retreated to the cooker, which gave her a chance to compose herself. The intense physical attraction which sparked between them was something totally unfamiliar to her. She had seen good-looking men before and admired them, but she had never before met a man who woke such alarmingly primitive responses in her. It seemed Greg only had to look at her with those narrowed dark eyes and a strange, throbbing heat began to pulsate through her entire body. The sensation was dangerous, unfamiliar and deeply disturbing. Rose felt a wild impulse to race out of the house, slamming the door behind her, and never, ever see Greg Trelawney again. She felt an even wilder impulse to slink up behind him, put her arms around his body and hug him so hard that her breasts were crushed provocatively against his back. What was happening to

her? Was she losing her mind? With a faint groan she
began to turn the handle of the coffee grinder, taking
out her frustration on the beans until the rich aroma of
ground coffee filled the room. Meanwhile Greg had been
busy at the cooker. Rose made more toast and then
hovered in the doorway, as far away from Greg as she
could decently stand without looking absurd.

'Can we eat in the conservatory?' she asked in an un-
naturally bright voice. 'I like looking at the sea and,
besides, I have some sketch plans of my cottage that I
want to show you.'

To Rose's relief, once they were safely settled in the
conservatory, the atmosphere between them seemed less
feverish. They ate their eggs and bacon and drank their
coffee with the sketches scattered all over the table so
that they could argue while they had their meal. Even
that had a certain curious charm for Rose. She had lived
on her own for several years and had never realised how
much she craved the simple pleasure of a man's company
at breakfast.

Luckily Greg was no longer giving her unsettling
glances, but was directing all his frowning intensity to
her sketch plans of the cottage. She noticed that he was
wearing one of the infamous red shirts that had caused
her so much soul searching and for a moment was
tempted to tackle him on the subject. The words quivered
on her tongue, but she bit them back. To confront him
now would only plunge them both back into the seething
emotional turmoil that she wanted to avoid. No, it was
better to let the whole issue drop and keep the atmosphere light between them. She must try and view Greg
as a friend, who was simply giving her a tradesman's
sound advice on her home improvements. In this he was
very successful. She was both annoyed and pleased to
find that he came up with several brilliant suggestions
which would never have occurred to her. When they had

cleared the table, he shuffled all their sketch plans into a pile and clipped a handwritten note about her final decisions on top.

'Right,' he said briskly. 'If you're happy with that, we'll drop it all off to John Gleeson the builder as we go through Polperro. You couldn't do better than employ him. He'll give you a fair price, do honest work and subcontract all the plumbing and wiring, so you'll have nothing to do but put your signature on the paper. Agreed?'

'Agreed,' said Rose, feeling rather taken aback at the speed with which Greg operated.

'Good. Then let's go to the beach,' he urged. 'Charlie's staying at Plymouth for the weekend with his girlfriend and he's lent me his car, so when you get sick of the sea we can drive around and see a bit of the countryside.'

Charlie's car smelt of rubber and seaweed, but Rose was too excited to care as she climbed into the passenger seat and tossed her denim beach-bag into the back. Now that the decisions about the cottage were out of the way, she felt like a child on holiday, relaxed, brimming with high spirits and anxious to enjoy every moment. And that wasn't hard to do in Cornwall.

After a quick trip to John Gleeson's house, where she signed some papers, they drove on to Talland Bay, where they parked the car on a grassy expanse overlooking the beach. It was another fine, hot day and the shouts of excited children rose to meet them as they picked their way down the sandy path to the shore. The air was warm and filled with the mingled scent of gorse bushes and salt, and Rose felt the tension of the previous months beginning to evaporate like a sea mist in the hot sun.

'Let's go over on the far side,' suggested Greg. 'There's shade there from the rocks, or you can sit in the sun if you prefer, and it looks a bit quieter away from the kids.'

Rose followed him over the beach, enjoying the way the gritty sand crunched underfoot, the tug of the wind in her hair, the vivid colours of the sea, deep blue in the distance and emerald-green close to shore just before it splashed in a lacy border of foam. She still felt quite tired and disoriented by the long trip from Australia and the hectic activity of her first few days in Britain, so the prospect of a lazy day by the beach was sheer bliss.

'Where do you want to sit?' Greg asked her. 'In the sun or the shade?'

Rose pulled a face. 'Ten minutes in the sun and then I'll move into the shade,' she announced. 'I burn easily.'

'You'd better put some sunscreen on. Do you want me to help you?'

I'm not sure that I should have agreed to this, thought Rose dreamily five minutes later as she lay face down on a towel in the hot sand with Greg massaging sunscreen into her back. A brief blue two-piece swimsuit seemed like a very inadequate barrier against those disturbingly skilful, caressing fingers. But while her mind might have grave misgivings, her body didn't. She lay purring softly like a drowsing kitten, uttering little mews of pleasure as Greg's hands moved in circles of fire over her body.

'Turn over,' he instructed.

A hot rush of colour flooded her cheeks. This was even worse! She gasped, sat up and reached out her hand for the bottle.

'I—I can manage the front myself,' she stammered.

'Don't be so prissy, Rose!' exclaimed Greg in disgust. 'It's only sunscreen.'

Rose said nothing, but doggedly continued to hold out her hand for the bottle. Instead of relenting, Greg held it tantalisingly out of reach.

'Care to fight me for it?' he mocked.

Rose's eyes flashed with annoyance and she glanced around at the crowded beach. 'No, I wouldn't,' she muttered between her teeth, cringing at the thought of the scene that would follow.

'Pity,' mourned Greg, gazing at her from under half-closed eyelids with a sultry expression that made every nerve in her body quiver. 'It might have been rather fun. Well, if you're not going to fight me for it, you'll have to lie down and let me do what I want with you, won't you?'

'You manipulative brute!' breathed Rose indignantly. 'And what if I decide to go home?'

'It's a long walk,' murmured Greg, clearly enjoying this battle of words. 'You'd be much wiser just to lie down, close your eyes and think of the Empire.'

That made Rose give an unwilling gasp of laughter and the contest was over. Still simmering with resentment at her defeat, but unable to quench a bubble of laughter, she lay down in a pose of rigid self-sacrifice and deliberately assumed a grim expression.

'I'm thinking of the Empire,' she said defiantly.

But she didn't think of the Empire as Greg squeezed the warm, creamy liquid into his palm and begun to rub it in smooth, fluid strokes across her belly, over her chest and up and down on the ripe, swelling curve of her breasts above the flimsy bikini top. Partly to avoid meeting Greg's gaze, Rose closed her eyes, but that was a mistake. The images that filled her mind weren't of duty and self-sacrifice at all, but of a frenzied pleasure more intense and more thrilling than anything she could ever imagine. By the time Greg had finished massaging her, prolonging the exquisite torment with a brisk, tingling rub of the soles of her feet, she felt as if her whole body was in the grip of a fever. Every muscle was clenched agonisingly, her breath was coming in shallow gulps and an unfamiliar, aching sense of need was coursing through her.

'Your turn,' said Greg, handing her the bottle with a sly smile.

'What do you mean, my turn?' she demanded indignantly.

'Time to get your own back. Don't you want to rub me?'

'No,' retorted Rose scathingly.

Yet she did, that was the awful thing. Darting a hasty, furtive glance at Greg's virile body clad in the briefest of black bathing trunks, she felt a crazy, intoxicating urge to accept his invitation, to push him back on the towel, hot from the sun, and rub that slick, creamy lotion over the hard, rippling muscles of his belly and those long, suntanned, hair-roughened legs. She wanted to make him lie face down so she could straddle his body with her legs and stroke and tease and glory in the hard, muscular strength of his back. And that wasn't all she wanted. She wanted to lie beside him and kiss him, feel his warm mouth, tasting of salt, mingle with hers, feel the velvety caress of his fingers between her thighs just as she had felt it a moment before when he was applying the sunscreen. Rose was appalled at the things she wanted.

'No, thank you,' she added primly. 'I'd rather read my book.'

And, squeezing herself into a defensive huddle with her knees drawn up, as if she were trying to avoid death from hypothermia, Rose did exactly that. Greg watched her with amusement for a moment, then carelessly dolloped some sunscreen on his own body, rubbed it in and lay down to sunbathe. After a while his eyes closed as if he was asleep and Rose let out a ragged sigh of relief, dropped her book and stretched out flat on her back herself. Heavens, this was more nerve-racking than doing final exams at university... Soon her own eyelids began to droop and she sat up with a jolt to find that Greg was watching her with an unmistakable look of brooding desire on his face. Hastily he closed his eyes as she frowned at him.

Torn between an urge to burst out laughing or lose her temper, Rose opened her denim bag, slipped on her blue shorts and a white T-shirt, then put a straw hat on her head and ostentatiously moved her towel away into the shade. She thought she heard Greg heave a faint sigh of disappointment. Yet as the day wore on she could not manage to stay annoyed with him, since she felt so relaxed and at ease in his company. Early in the afternoon the heat of the sun drove them into the water to cool off and Greg swam powerfully and effortlessly like a seal, while Rose shivered in the shallows.

'Come on,' he urged, shaking his wet, dark hair out of his eyes. 'It's gorgeous in here. Really warm once you get used to it. These waters are part of the Gulf Stream, you know.'

'Really warm?' bleated Rose, taking another heroic step three inches further into the water. 'You must be joking! Only a polar bear would call this water warm.'

With a sudden flashing violence, Greg surged out of the water, seized her wrist and put an end to the argument by dragging her down with him. For a moment she gasped and fought as a cloud of bubbles exploded in the chill green water around her. Then his arms came around her and a giddy sense of exhilaration took hold of her as they shot to the surface together.

It was late afternoon when at last they decided to leave the beach and, in spite of the suncreen, Rose's face was beginning to tingle warningly. All the same, she couldn't remember ever having a more marvellous day. This is crazy, she told herself sternly as they crunched up the sand together. You can't afford to encourage Greg when he keeps flirting with you so outrageously. He'll get the wrong idea. But an unfamiliar part of her mind answered defiantly, what if he does? You're old enough to take care of yourself, aren't you? Anyway, maybe he'd be getting the right idea. Rose winced at her own thoughts. It was as if moving to Cornwall had unleashed a whole new and unfamiliar identity for her. She felt wild, sensual, a fitting partner for the man striding beside her. Not a tame woman any more, but a woman ready to take risks...

'Well, now what would you like to do?' demanded Greg. 'Home for a shower and then a Chinese meal in Looe?'

'Sounds good to me,' agreed Rose.

In compliment to Greg, she wore the embroidered sweater and the soft blue muslin skirt when they went out to dinner. Greg himself was casually but impeccably dressed in beige drill trousers and a striped beige and brown short-sleeved shirt. When they were shown into a secluded booth in the restaurant they both leaned back, sighed and smiled at each other with the ease of two people totally at home in each other's company.

'Something to drink?' invited Greg.

'Mm, please,' agreed Rose. 'About half a gallon of orange juice with lots of ice.'

'All right,' nodded Greg, leafing through the wine list. 'I'll have a gin and tonic and then something to go with the meal. I don't know about you, my love, but I think only a light white wine goes well with Chinese food. Perhaps a Vernaccia Bianca from Italy. What do you think?'

'Yes, all right,' agreed Rose, rather impressed by the knowledgeable way that Greg had pronounced the Italian name.

'Now what about the serious question of food?' he asked.

'I'd like some wan tun soup,' said Rose. 'Or maybe some spring rolls as a starter, but after that do you think we could get one or two dishes to share?'

'Why not? The Peking duck here is very good, I can recommend it. So how about that with some chilli beef and vegetables, honeyed prawns and steamed rice?'

'Yum!' she said ecstatically.

When the waitress brought their drinks and had taken the rest of their order, Rose leaned back in her chair and heaved a sigh of pleasure.

'I'm having such a wonderful time this weekend,' she announced dreamily, 'that I can hardly believe things were so awful only a few weeks ago. It all seems like a bad dream now, jumbled, unpleasant, not quite real.'

'Do you miss him?' asked Greg abruptly.

Rose's face shadowed. She gave a faint groan and traced a pattern round the rim of her orange-juice glass with her finger. Her thoughts went winging back to Martin and she felt a rush of humiliation, yearning and hurt pride.

'Not when I'm busy,' she admitted. 'As long as I keep occupied, I don't have to think about him and it hardly hurts at all. But I suspect it would be a different matter if I ever saw him again. I'd probably be right back where I was a little while ago. Hating him for being so callous, but still wanting him unbearably.'

'That's insane,' growled Greg. 'He treated you abominably.'

'I know,' agreed Rose with a sigh. 'But falling in love doesn't make people act reasonably, does it?'

'No, it certainly doesn't,' retorted Greg. 'So it's probably a good thing that your rotten ex-lover is safely on the other side of the world. But just tell me this. Once you're properly over it and the whole thing really does seem like a distant nightmare, what then?'

'What do you mean?' asked Rose, frowning.

At that moment the waitress arrived with Rose's soup and Greg's spring rolls so that they were forced to interrupt their discussion. Yet while the girl fussed around with blue and white patterned rice bowls, chopsticks, china spoons and a container of sweet, sticky sauce, Greg's eyes smouldered with inquisitorial fervour.

'I mean exactly what I say,' he burst out when the waitress had left. 'What do you intend to do once you've recovered from this wretched Martin? Are you going to look for a more suitable lover?'

Rose snorted. 'What's a more suitable lover?' she demanded tartly.

'Someone like me.'

The audacity of it took her breath away. She gave him a swift, stricken look, hoping to find that he was joking. But his dark eyes met hers with a smoky, sensual urgency that killed the hope at once.

'You're not serious?' she faltered.

'On the contrary, I'm intensely serious. I want you, Rose Ashley. And I always get what I want.'

Anger flowed into Rose's veins, hot and rich and useful.

'Don't talk about me like that!' she flared. 'Don't talk about what you want as if I were some object you could snatch. I'm a person with feelings and needs and desires of my own. A person you've only just met. You don't even know anything about me.'

Greg looked at her with an odd, brooding smile. 'You're wrong,' he growled. 'I know a lot about you, Rose. Your fears, your hopes, your good qualities and your bad. And I know the most important thing of all about you.'

'What's that?' she snapped.

He leaned towards her and his voice was so low that she could scarcely catch it. A deep, hoarse secret for her ears alone. 'That you want me just as violently as I want you. And it's been like that from the first moment we saw each other in the pub.'

Rose's face flamed. 'And you think that's a good enough reason for us to go to bed together?' she hissed furiously.

'What better one could there possibly be?' taunted Greg.

'How about love? Respect? Marriage?' cried Rose, almost spitting the words at him.

Greg shrugged, his dark eyes inscrutable.

'Those things are all very well in their place,' he conceded. 'But the most primitive, violent, basic instinct of all is what really counts. The need like a fire in the blood when a man and woman have to have each other, when they'd throw away everything else just for one night of fire together!'

Rose dropped her eyes uncomfortably. She disapproved of everything Greg was saying and yet she could not help being stirred by his words. His gaze seemed to be scorching her . . .

'That's ridiculous!' she protested. 'It's only self-indulgence. I'd never stoop to that, no matter how much I——'

'No matter how much you wanted me?' taunted Greg. 'Now there's an interesting admission.'

'I didn't admit anything!'

'You didn't have to. It's been in every look and smile and movement you've made since I've met you. We want each other rather badly, don't we, my love?'

She wished Greg wouldn't say these things to her, wouldn't send her reeling off balance like this. His frankness outraged her, but at the same time she couldn't help feeling unexpectedly thrilled to learn that Greg did want her just as badly as she wanted him, that he was driven by the same reckless impulse of passion. Not that she had any intention of acting on her impulses. It would be sheer lunacy to give in and take him as her lover when they hardly even knew each other... She thrust away the thought that they already seemed to know each other more deeply than many couples did after a lifetime. It was that very sense of immediate intimacy which had sprung up between them that made Greg so dangerous, not only because he made her heart race with desire, but also because he slipped under her defences. Unlike any other man she had ever met, he seemed to have an uncanny ability to sense her innermost feelings. That made her feel frighteningly vulnerable. Especially when he gazed at her with those searching dark eyes that seemed to see right into her soul...

'Well,' he prompted, 'don't you feel it too?'

'Don't ask me!' she said jerkily.

'Why not?' demanded Greg. 'It's important, isn't it?'

Her eyes met his in a tormented glance and then darted away. 'Yes,' she admitted. 'But I don't know you well enough to be sure of my feelings towards you.'

'Of course you do. Don't stop to think about it, Rose, answer me from the heart. Do you want me?'

'Yes. Yes...no! Oh, stop it, Greg! It's not that simple.'

'Why not?'

She tossed her head, shaking her loose, tumbled brown hair over her shoulders. Why couldn't Greg be content with meaningless small talk like normal people? Why did he have to insist on splintering all her defences and rampaging through to her naked, unprotected heart? Her whole body tensed as she fought off the unhappy childhood memories of her father and the equally bad memories of Martin.

'Are you asking me to become your lover?' she demanded in a tormented voice.

'Yes.'

'I can't!'

'Why not?' he asked, as if nothing could be simpler.

'Because I haven't known you long enough. And because——'

'It doesn't have to happen immediately,' Greg assured her, his eyes filled with blazing light. 'Although personally I'd like nothing better than to take you home this very night and make passionate love to you, Rose. But I can wait, although I'm not naturally a patient man. What I couldn't bear was to go on without telling you how I felt.'

'That's all very well,' said Rose in an exasperated voice. 'But you seem to think it's just like ordering something at a shop. You tell me politely that you'll wait and then sit back and expect me to give you some kind of delivery date. That's insane!'

'Why?' demanded Greg.

'Because I don't take relationships as lightly as you evidently do!' retorted Rose. 'I don't ever want another lover, unless I'm quite certain that I intend to marry him.'

'I thought you had no intention of marrying,' Greg reminded her with a frown. 'That's what you told me the other day outside the church at Talland.'

Rose gave an exasperated sigh. Why did men have to be so literal-minded? Why could they only ever grasp what a woman said and not what she meant?

'I probably won't ever get married,' she replied with a toss of her head. 'But if I do remain single, I certainly won't be fool enough to get entangled with another man. And even if I did want to marry, I'd have to be very, very sure of the man I was marrying.'

'Sure of him?' echoed Greg. 'What do you mean by that?'

Rose bit her lip. 'Sure that I could trust him,' she replied. 'What I've seen of men so far doesn't impress me with their trustworthiness. Look at my father with all his mean little infidelities, or Martin, dedicated to making money above all else and trampling over women as if they were only there to serve him and didn't have any feelings of their own. I couldn't live with that kind of pain and suspicion. I'd rather do without marriage entirely than put up with being deceived or exploited.'

Greg suddenly became very busy with the plate of spring rolls, picking up one of the crisp morsels in his chopsticks and dipping it intently into the sweet and sour sauce as if he was only half listening to Rose. She felt a pang of annoyance. After all, he was the one who had started this conversation!

'I'm sorry if I'm boring you,' she said in an offended tone.

He looked up at that, his eyes dark and piercing and mercilessly direct. 'No, you don't bore me,' he said. 'You intrigue me. You're frightened of men, aren't you, Rose? And frightened of yourself?'

'What do you mean?' she asked sharply.

'What fascinated me about you right from the start was the conflict that was obviously raging inside you. So precise, so prim, so polite, so dull! And yet beneath it I could sense the real you, passionate, impetuous, turbulent and far, far more interesting, but afraid to let yourself go. Well, having heard about your father and your lover, I understand why you're hurt and suspicious and I can see that you try and make life safe for yourself by being very controlled and logical but it won't work, my dear. Life isn't like that, love isn't like that, and you're taking things all the wrong way.'

'Oh?' said Rose coldly. 'And what should I do, according to you?'

Greg leaned forward and touched one of the silky strands of brown hair that was dangling down the front of her sweater.

'Trust your instincts,' he urged. 'Let yourself go. Take risks with life. It will be worth it, Rose, believe me.'

Rose wanted to sneer at him, to retreat, to say that he was quite wrong about her and that she really was as cool and sensible as she seemed on the surface. But for some reason she couldn't do it, perhaps because she knew deep down that Greg was right and that he understood her more profoundly than any other human being had ever done. She gazed back at him in torment, and slowly shook her head, as if she was refusing some invitation too terrifying and exalting to contemplate.

'Just go with the flow,' he whispered. 'Let it happen, Rose, don't say no to life.'

At that moment the waitress appeared to remove the empty bowls and serve their main course, and Greg released her hand.

Rose felt dizzy with relief at this unexpected reprieve, but gradually realised that nothing had changed. Although Greg's manner had now lost its intensity and he was chatting amiably, helping her to the choicest titbits of chili beef and crisp, savoury Peking duck, it was as if he had woven some potent spell around her that still continued to exert its subtle magic. The rest of the room seemed as shadowy and unreal as a film set, the other diners no more than unimportant extras, as all her attention focused magnetically on Greg. She tried to remind herself that she must tread carefully, must resist his allure, but it was useless. How could she resist someone who seemed to know everything there was to know about her? And who saw beneath her cool, sensible façade to the passionate creature she had always known existed beneath? Rose had never felt such a heady sense of abandon before. Her head was swimming, her face was flushed from the sun and the wine, and she had the intoxicating sense that at any moment she might yield to Greg's command and stop being afraid of life. And she knew that if that happened she would simply fall dizzily and helplessly in love with him. Even now she wanted him with an intensity that shocked and elated her. It would be easy to surrender to him, fatally easy, as easy and urgent as breathing. The empty plates were taken away and replaced by almond cookies and green tea, then gradually those too vanished. At last Greg's warm, strong fingers closed over hers.

'Ready to go?' he asked.

Rose felt as if she were floating as they went down the stairs and along the echoing road that led to the car park. She had only had two glasses of wine, so it couldn't be that, but she felt as if all the normal bonds of convention which constrained her were somehow dissolving and falling away. It was still twilight outside, a mysterious shadowy green twilight that made the lights of houses and fishing boats sparkle like necklaces. As they drove across the bridge to West Looe and emerged into open countryside the scent of freshly cut hay and salt air wafted into the car and filled her lungs. Her feelings were a strange blend of excitement and profound tranquillity and when Greg gave her a stormy sideways glance she smiled back at him without any of her usual reserve. Just for this one night she felt a wildness in her blood, an impatience with the cautious, defensive way she had lived her life until now. It might be madness, but she felt that whatever happened between her and Greg would be deeply, awesomely right. As inevitable and fitting as the arrival of dawn or the falling of leaves in autumn. Something that was part of the primitive rhythm of life and far too natural to be feared or regretted. For the first time in her life Rose was conscious of her power as a woman and the knowledge transfigured her. Every cell in her body seemed roused into a firestorm of hunger and yearning, an urgent, pulsating need. As they approached the cottage on the cliff-top, she let out her breath in a soft sigh, stretched back luxuriously into the seat and closed her eyes, rather enjoying the way that the world seemed to be spinning wildly about her, completely out of control.

Greg stopped the car in the driveway and came round to the passenger door. With the touch of his hand on her shoulder, Rose's eyes flew open.

'Are you feeling all right?' he demanded.

Her breast heaved as she sought for words to answer him and she felt as if her whole body was throbbing and aching with unsatisfied need. A wry smile touched the corners of her mouth.

'I could say that it's too much wine or too much sun or too much jet-lag,' she said huskily. 'But I don't think it's any of those things really. I think it must be pure midsummer madness that's making me feel this way.'

Greg's hand cupped her chin and he looked deep into her eyes with a hungry expression of yearning. 'How do you feel?' he growled.

Some vestige of her old caution overtook her and she flushed and looked away. 'I can't tell you,' she mumbled.

His hand touched her cheek, forcing her head back. 'Look at me,' he ordered. 'Would it help if I tell you how I feel? That this is going to be the most important thing in both our lives? But you already know that, don't you?'

A shudder went through her and she gave a small, assenting nod. Catching her by the hair, he looked fiercely into her eyes.

'You can trust me, Rose,' he growled. 'Whatever happens, I swear you can trust me.' Then, seizing her hands, he drew her out of the car, slammed the door and hurried her into the house. There, as if driven by a common impulse, they fell into each other's arms. Fire seemed to blaze through Rose's veins as Greg hauled her urgently against him. She could feel the hard, muscular strength of his powerful body through the thin fabric of his clothes and the violent, irregular thudding of his

heart. Threading his fingers through her hair, he tilted
back her head and kissed her full on her softly gasping
mouth. Her lips quivered and then parted to welcome
him in. An aching sweetness flooded through her at the
warm, demanding hardness of his kisses and her eyes
fluttered shut. She felt her body sway enticingly against
him and heard his muffled groan as she brushed the most
secret part of him. Seizing her by the hips, he ground
her body ruthlessly against him, demanding more. A low
whimper of longing escaped her and she let him do as
he wanted with her, glorying in the merciless caress of
his hands as they moved in hectic spirals over her quivering body. When he peeled the sweater over her head
and tossed it carelessly on the floor, she did not offer
any resistance but watched him from under half-closed
lids, feeling every part of her throb with urgent need.
Then he slipped his hands inside her thin T-shirt and
cupped her warm, full breasts.

'My beautiful, darling Rose,' he breathed. 'Do you
know how much I want you?'

A shudder of pure, tingling delight rippled through
her as his fingertips stroked her nipples, and she nodded
wordlessly.

'Let me take it off,' he said hoarsely and, as deftly as
if they had been lovers forever, he drew the T-shirt over
her head, slipped off her bra and gazed down at her with
a wild, hungry longing in his eyes.

'Greg——' she murmured unsteadily.

'Oh, Rose, I didn't mean this to be so soon, but you
don't know what you do to me. You're driving me crazy,
my love. Let me touch you, hold you, drown in you.'

With a low groan he sank on one knee, gripped her
waist as if he would snap it in two and buried his face
in her breasts. The warm tickle of his breath, the thrilling
tug of his mouth on her nipple made her cry out with
longing and she flung her arms around him and nuzzled

his head. He smelled clean and fresh and primitively
virile, with an aroma of salt and shampoo and some
strange, herbal masculine scent that brought a flood of
warmth pulsating through her.

'Greg——' she gasped again.

'I've wanted to do this from the first moment I saw
you. Oh, you're gorgeous, Rose. Warm and soft and
giving, totally feminine…we belong together, you know
that, don't you?' Rose's breath was coming in shallow
gulps and a firestorm of aching, throbbing desire was
beginning to ignite in every cell of her body when suddenly there was a disturbance. A vigorous knocking at
the conservatory door, followed by a loud hail.

'Hello! Anybody home?'

She froze in panic as Greg leapt to his feet, swearing
colourfully under his breath. With a final, exasperated
oath he snatched up her clothes from the floor and
bundled them into her arms.

'Who is it?' mouthed Rose, blushing hotly.

'Hugh Thomas, the bank manager. Run upstairs and
get dressed and I'll try and get rid of him.'

Overwhelmed by shock, embarrassment and a turbulent mixture of relief and vexation, Rose scuttled up
the stairs, but halfway up she gave a muffled cry of
dismay as she saw that her bra was still lying blatantly
in the middle of the hall carpet. Hastily she changed
direction, ran back down and snatched it up. But at that
moment she heard voices approaching from the direction of the conservatory.

'Oh, no!' wailed Rose under her breath. And, without
pausing to think, she dived into the kitchen. The voices
came closer, with Hugh's lilting tones overriding Greg's.

'No trouble at all,' he insisted. 'We've got more
strawberries than we can eat this time of the year, so I
thought you'd like a few. I'll just put them in the kitchen
for you.'

Rose gasped. This was getting worse and worse! Wildly she looked around for an avenue of escape and her eye lit on the utility-room door. Clutching her disordered clothes against her naked breasts, she darted out of sight just a second before Greg and Hugh entered the kitchen from the hallway. There was a light thud as Hugh evidently dropped a couple of punnets of strawberries on the kitchen table, followed by the scraping of a chair as he made himself at home.

'Actually, Hugh, I'm rather busy,' began Greg.

'Not too busy to listen to me, boyo,' said Hugh sternly. 'Now listen, Greg, the strawberries are only an excuse and you know it. What I really want is a word with you.'

Rose winced and, as quietly as she could, began to pull on her bra and T-shirt. This sounded as if it could be a long conversation, damn it!

'A word with me... What about?'

'Ingrid.'

'Ingrid?' echoed Greg in an exasperated voice. 'What's Ingrid been doing?'

'Well, in the first place,' said Hugh, 'she came round to me in a great fuss and bother this afternoon because she'd been looking for you and couldn't find you.'

'I was out.'

'Yes, that's all very well. But she had an important fax from Copenhagen to do with some shipping plans that needed your attention urgently. Now I've told you before, Greg, and I'll tell you again. It's ridiculous for a man in your position to shut yourself away like this every weekend out of the reach of a telephone and a fax machine. You can't go on living this way when you've got a business to run.'

'I like living this way,' insisted Greg stubbornly.

Hugh gave a snort of bitter laughter. 'Perhaps you do, but you put your friends and your employees to a lot of trouble tracking you down. Not to mention your faithful old bank manager. But that's not all I want to talk to you about. What I want to know is what you're up to with young Ingrid.'

'I'm not up to anything!' snapped Greg.

'Well, that's not what she tells me,' retorted Hugh suspiciously. 'The poor kid's in love with you, Greg, and if you've been taking advantage of her I'll horsewhip you, you black-hearted bastard.'

'I have not taken advantage of her!' hissed Greg, slamming his fist down on the table. 'And I'll thank you to mind your own business, Hugh Thomas.'

'Humph,' sniffed Hugh. 'Well, that may be true, and it may not. But I've seen you playing fast and loose with women for years, Greg Trelawney, and I've got another bone to pick with you. What kind of game are you playing with that young Australian lass?'

'Mind your own business,' growled Greg.

'You know what a village is like, Greg,' warned Hugh. 'Everyone's business is common knowledge. And you're up to something with that girl. Why else would you offer to guarantee a bank loan for her, when you know I could never have given it to her otherwise? And why all the play-acting? I've heard all about you, paying Charlie Polglaze to lend you his awful old wreck of a car when you've got a perfectly good Rolls sitting there in your garage untouched. What I want to know is this: why are you trying to convince that poor girl that you're nothing but a simple fisherman, when all the time you're one of the richest men in England?'

CHAPTER FIVE

ROSE reeled with shock at Hugh's words as all her ideas about Greg were suddenly turned upside-down. What did Hugh mean? Could Greg really be one of the richest men in England, and why on earth hadn't he told her? But before she could sort out the tumult of questions that whirled frantically in her mind, Greg began to speak.

'Look, Hugh, you've been a damned good friend to me and an honest, reliable bank manager, but my private life is none of your business and I don't intend to discuss it with you. Now, if you'll excuse me, I was very busy when you arrived and I've got urgent matters to deal with, so can I catch up with you in the office later in the week?'

Urgent matters? thought Rose, beginning to simmer furiously. He makes me sound like a business deal he wants to get rid of as soon as possible! Well, I've got a few questions I want answered first. How dare he? How dare he deceive me like that?

The sound of voices receded down the hall and out into the conservatory. Rose heard the distant slamming of a door and the sound of a car engine starting up, then Greg came back into the hall.

'Rose?' he shouted up the stairs.

Deliberately she opened the laundry door and stood there with eyes flashing. 'I'm right here!' she called in a dangerous voice.

Greg came back into the kitchen wearing a baffled frown. 'In the laundry?' he said. 'What are you doing there?'

'Nothing. Just thinking about a certain simple fisherman.'

Greg looked as if his dentist had just hit a raw nerve. 'Oh, you heard that, did you?' he asked uneasily. 'I was afraid you might. Listen, my love, seeing that you're in there anyway, did my blue jeans come through the tumble-drier?'

'Don't you "my love" me!' hissed Rose. 'You brute! You lying, unscrupulous, double-dealing brute! Are you really rich?'

Greg's face wore a hunted look. 'Yes,' he agreed apologetically.

'Then why didn't you tell me before?' demanded Rose.

'I was trying to impress you.'

Rose gave a gasp of half-hysterical laughter. 'Trying to impress me? By driving around in a car full of lobster pots and gumboots? By pretending that you didn't have enough money to lend me for a taxi fare? Trying to impress me?'

'Yes.'

'Could I ask why?'

'I thought it was what you wanted,' said Greg. 'A simple, honest fisherman.'

'Honest? Honest! That's a laugh!'

'A simple, honest fisherman,' continued Greg, turning the full power of his brooding dark eyes on her. 'Who would share the romance of Cornwall with you, someone who wasn't obsessed with money like the last man you were involved with. Someone whose motives towards you were honorable.'

'Honourable?' croaked Rose. 'Oh, sure!'

'My motives were honourable,' insisted Greg. 'Well, fairly honourable. Anyway, I thought I was doing you a favour, playing things the way you wanted them. Smugglers, fishermen, ye olde Englande, that sort of thing.'

'A favour! You patronising——! And to think I actually believed all that guff about your leaving school when you were fifteen, being apprenticed to a boat builder, going off to work in the North Sea fishing fleet.'

'It's all true,' protested Greg. 'I just didn't tell you what happened next.'

Rose snorted. 'Well, what did happen next?' she demanded.

'Oh, I bought a second fishing boat and then a third. Then I took out a huge loan and bought the shipyard. And I really made it pay.'

'And now?' asked Rose with grudging interest. 'What are you now?'

Greg shrugged impatiently. 'I'm a simple fisherman and boat builder, just as I always was. The only difference is that now I own a shipyard and a fishing fleet. But that doesn't matter, Rose. It's never mattered much to me and it shouldn't matter to you. What happened between us was real enough. All right, I admit I lied to you, but it was harmless. Just a crazy impulse.'

'Impulse nothing!' said Rose through her teeth. 'It was calculated deceit! Just the way it was with that shirt.'

'Shirt?' echoed Greg in bewilderment.

'Yes!' she blazed. 'The shirt that mysteriously changed colour after you came ashore at my cottage. It had a navy stripe when you left the boat and a green stripe the following morning, which suggests to my simple mind that there were two shirts. It also suggests that you intended to stay the night with me right from the very beginning.'

'Oh, so you noticed that, did you?' asked Greg in an admiring voice.

'Yes, and I should have realised then how scheming you were. I also noticed how the Cornish accent got stronger once I told you how much I liked the simple village life. And now that I come to think of it, I noticed how you didn't want me to talk to Joan about you. I suppose you were afraid she'd spill the beans, weren't you? Oh, God, I was a fool to trust you!'

'Don't say that,' protested Greg. 'I was going to tell you the truth, Rose, honestly.'

'Oh, yes? When?'

'After——' Greg began. Then he stopped abruptly and stared reflectively at the ceiling.

'After you'd got me into bed with you and had what you wanted?' demanded Rose in derision. 'And then you would have said thanks very much and pushed off, wouldn't you? Because you'd be far too rich and important to stick around with someone like me!'

Suddenly Greg seized her by the shoulders.

'Rose, no!' he cried in an appalled voice. 'It wasn't like that, believe me!'

'Believe you?' shouted Rose. 'I'll never believe another word you say to me!' She twisted out of his grip and as she did so her sweater pulled out of shape. She stared down at it as if she were seeing it for the first time.

'That's another thing,' she gasped. 'I thought you were so nice buying me this when you really couldn't afford it, but it was all just a game to you, wasn't it? A little more bait in the trap. Well, you can just have it back!' With a swift, angry movement she hauled the garment over her head and flung it in Greg's face.

'Are you going to throw the skirt at me too?' he asked hopefully.

But instead of laughing Rose let out a low groan and burst suddenly and noisily into tears. Her whole body shook and she had to clutch hold of the washing-machine for support, for in that appalling moment she had suddenly discovered how much this meant to her. She had been on the brink of falling in love with Greg and yet he had betrayed her, just like Martin. Except that this time it was worse, far worse, this time she felt as if the whole world was breaking up around her. Not even bothering to hide her misery, she closed her eyes, bit her lip and let the scalding tears flow unchecked down her cheeks. Looking exasperated, Greg hauled her into his arms and hugged her. She tried to struggle but he was too strong for her. There was nothing overtly sexual in that contact, just a warm, reassuring closeness. And even now, fool that she was, Rose ached to remain in his arms. But she mustn't! She must break away, fight this insidious attraction, remind herself of how he had used and deceived her. Her chin came up and she blinked back the tears, thrusting him away from her with a savage push. As she did so, a fresh grievance came to her mind.

'Just as a matter of interest,' she said in a hostile voice, 'who's Ingrid?'

'Nobody,' growled Greg impatiently. 'Nobody important. A girl who works for me.'

And if I were fool enough to give in to him, that's what I'd be before very long, thought Rose dully, as soon as the next girl comes along and takes his eye. Who's Rose? Oh, nobody important, a girl who lives in my cottage or used to. I'll get rid of her for you, my love.

'Is she blonde? Does she drive a pink sports car?' she asked with barely suppressed venom.

'Yes, but how did you know?'

'I saw you with her in Polperro on Tuesday when you were supposedly fetching my bags from Pisky Bay.'

'I did fetch them. And I'd just come ashore at the harbour and put them in Charlie's car when Ingrid arrived in search of me. She claimed she had something urgent to tell me, so I let her drive me around Polperro while we talked. But it wasn't genuinely urgent. It never is with Ingrid.'

'Oh, what does it matter?' cried Rose irritably. 'No, don't touch me, Greg, I'm all right now.' Snatching her handkerchief out of the clean laundry basket, she scrubbed her eyes and blew her nose. Then, flashing Greg a look of burning contempt, she made a move towards the kitchen but found he was barring her way.

'Where are you going?'

'To pack.'

'Why?'

'Because I'm leaving!'

'You can't do that, Rose!'

'I can do anything I damn well like, Greg. I'm a grown woman and I don't have to stay here and let you take advantage of me.'

'I'm sorry,' he muttered, looking more disgruntled than repentant. 'But why do you have to make such a fuss about it? I wasn't lying to you just so I could get you into bed. I have very strong feelings for you, Rose, and that's the truth, my love.'

'Nice line, Greg,' she said scornfully. 'Try it on the next girl who comes along. Perhaps you should take her into a smuggler's cellar too and give her a real thrill.'

'Rose, you can't go! We have too much to discuss.'

'We have nothing to discuss except how I'm getting out of this place. Would you be kind enough to call me a taxi? Oh, of course, you can't, can you? Simple fishermen don't have telephones.'

'Cut it out!' growled Greg. 'I'll deliver you to your cottage.'

'All right,' she agreed coldly. 'Since the alternative seems to be carrying my suitcases several miles along the cliff path, I accept, but I hope you don't expect me to thank you.'

'Rose, please——'

'No.'

Her mouth hardened again ten minutes later when they came out of the house and Greg unlocked the garage and reversed a gleaming Rolls-Royce into the driveway.

'Is this the old bomb that's forever breaking down?' she demanded tartly.

His eyes narrowed stormily, but he said nothing and the drive to Aunt Em's cottage passed in tense silence. When they arrived Rose met with another unexpected setback. By now it was dark but in the moonlight she could see that the old claw-footed bath and the fuel stove had already been ripped out and were lying on the front lawn. Evidently John Gleeson had lost no time in getting to work! Rose groaned inwardly as the complications of the whole disaster dawned on her—the building contract, the bank loan, Greg as her guarantor...

'Look, please change your mind, Rose,' he wheedled. 'You can see for yourself this place won't be fit to live in for weeks.'

Her mouth set in a stubborn line and a fighting light came into her eyes. 'I don't care! I'll go and stay at Joan Penwithick's cottage until I can start trading with the bed-and-breakfast place. And don't worry. I'll pay the bank loan back if it kills me. I wouldn't want my guarantor going into debt for me.'

Greg swore under his breath. 'I don't give a stuff about the bank loan. It's you I'm concerned about. When can I see you again, Rose?'

'Never!'

Luckily Joan had been as good as her word and Rose found the door key under the flowerpot just as she had promised. With trembling fingers she inserted it into the door and let herself inside the cottage. Greg stayed just long enough to see that she was safe and then drove away with a scream of tyres that made her wince. Switching on the light, she looked about her, but apart from noticing that Joan's cottage had all the modern comforts that her own lacked, she was too upset to take much notice of her surroundings. Even now she could not be-

lieve that Greg could have made such a fool of her. She
felt hurt and angry at the mere thought of the conversation she had overheard between him and Hugh. Yet
what might have happened if Hugh hadn't arrived? In
the mood she had been in, she might well have ended
up making love with Greg and she ought to be grateful
that at least she had escaped that final humiliation! Yet
strangely even that thought did not bring her the relief
it should have done. Although she was boiling with resentment against Greg, some treacherous part of her still
yearned for his touch, still wanted to go after him and
beg him to explain, beg him to come out with a few
more lies that would make it all right for her to go on
seeing him. Her own weakness and foolishness appalled
her. I must be more careful in future, she told herself
bitterly. I've had a narrow escape and I don't want to
go through something like that again. Well, it's not likely,
replied another part of her mind wryly. There aren't
many men as dangerously attractive as Greg Trelawney...

Rose groaned, set down her suitcases and went to explore the rest of Joan's cottage, feeling rather uncomfortable about poking around somebody else's
territory in her absence. Fortunately it didn't take her
long to find what was obviously the spare bedroom and
dump her possessions there. But what was she going to
do now? She didn't want to be a burden to Joan and
she would obviously have to do some serious thinking
about her plans for the future. Even when her own
cottage was ready, she was by no means sure that she
wanted to stay in it now. Not with Greg Trelawney just
across the headland in Polperro every weekend! But what
could she do? For two pins she would leave Cornwall
forever, but her mother was arriving soon and she
couldn't just leave her in the lurch. Her tired brain
whirled with possible solutions. Perhaps she should just
stay long enough to get her mother established and then

move to London and look for a job? Well, there was no use thinking about it any more tonight. The best thing she could do was get into bed, bury her head in the covers and try to forget that she had ever met Greg...

During the next few days Rose tried to bury her turbulent feelings in a flurry of activity on the cottage. There wasn't much she could do in the daytime while the builders were there amid the whine of power tools and clouds of plaster dust, but in the evenings she did go in and measure up the windows so that she could plan for new curtains. A day's shopping in Plymouth was followed by another pleasurable day at Joan's sewing-machine. On the Friday evening at sunset, when the builders had finished work for the week, she went over to inspect their progress. If anything, the house looked worse than before. The kitchen and bathroom were gutted and the whole place was covered in a thick blanket of plaster dust, but as she went from room to room a faint excitement began to stir in her. Yes, it would be a beautiful little house once it was finished and all the money spent on it would be well worthwhile. She left the sitting-room till last, haunted by memories of the way she had sat there in the firelight with Greg and of that electrifying kiss that had plunged her into this whole crazy situation, but when she pushed open the creaking door the room did not look frightening at all.

The builders had left the window open and the scent of honeysuckle drifted in from outside. Rose stood for a minute, listening to the distant shrieking of the gulls and the booming waves on the beach and rather enjoying the peaceful quality of the dying gold light that filled the room with lengthy shadows. Then something caught her eye on the old coffee-table next to the battered sofa. A splash of dark red colour above a white lace doily. Mystified, Rose crossed the room and let out a soft gasp. It was a bunch of roses, deep red, velvety roses, with a strong, sweet scent. She picked them up and pressed them to her face, inhaling their fresh, moist perfume. As she did so, a plain white card fluttered to the floor. Rose bent and picked it up and her heart almost stopped as she read the words.

'Forgive me.'

Nothing more, just those two, simple words, but she felt as if a stiletto had pierced her. A poignant wave of memories rushed over her. Greg in the inn in Polperro, Greg at the wheel of his yacht with the blood-red sail curved out in the wind, Greg kissing her in the firelight here in this very room. Greg urging her to trust him... but she couldn't, she couldn't trust him! Never again. And she couldn't keep these roses, although she didn't know what to do with them, either. Should she just leave them here to wither and die and be found by the builders on Monday morning? Suddenly the need for some violent action took over her and, gripping the bouquet as tightly as if she wanted to strangle it, she marched out of the back door, down the garden and along the road to the beach. There, on the silvery sands where Greg had drawn up the dinghy, she hurled the flowers in a violent arc into the sea. But a lazy wave brought them curling back towards her and she had to watch as they bobbed, grew sodden and ruined and were finally carried away by the waves. It wasn't her fault, and yet it made her feel oddly destructive, oddly guilty, as if she had destroyed something infinitely precious and special to her. As she strode stormily back to Joan's house, her teeth were gritted in a hard line.

'Oh, Greg, why did I ever meet you?' she muttered under her breath.

She found something to distract her thoughts a few days later with Joan's return from Dorset. Rose came back from talking with the builders one afternoon to find the older woman pegging washing on the line.

'Hello, Rose,' she cried cheerfully, setting down her peg basket and coming to kiss Rose on the cheek. 'I see you've made yourself at home. Well, I'm very happy to see you, my dear.'

'Yes, I'm sorry,' stammered Rose. 'You see, I decided you were right about Greg's place and——'

'No need to explain, my dear,' said Joan, although she ran a shrewd eye over Rose's flushed cheeks and downcast gaze. 'You just stay as long as you like. Now, come inside and we'll have a nice cup of tea and I'll show you the photos of my new grandson.'

While they were consuming hot scones with jam and cream and tea strong enough to stand a spoon up in, Rose suddenly blurted out the question which had been worrying her for several days.

'Joan, why did you say you didn't like to think of an impressionable young woman staying at Greg's place?'

Joan's eyes opened wide and gleamed with unmistakable excitement. She refilled her cup and leaned confidingly towards Rose, lowering her voice and glancing over her shoulder as if she might be overhead.

'Goings on!' she announced in hushed tones, although there was a certain admiring undertone beneath the disapproval. 'Why, you wouldn't credit it if I told you the goings on there had been in that cottage of his since his poor mother left! Greg came from a good, steady family, but he's always been too wrapped up in his business affairs to settle down and marry decently. To tell you the truth, I think the idea bored him. But he certainly hasn't gone without women because of it. Oh, no! Not that he's ever gone too far with any of the village girls—he'd have their father or brothers to answer to if he did. But women from London, that's a different story! And from further afield too, some of them foreigners even. There was a young girl no more than eighteen or nineteen staying at his cottage last summer and, when I came along the cliff path on my way to Polperro, there she was, as bold as brass, sunbathing on the back patio and not a stitch on! Can you believe it?'

'Not a stitch?' marvelled Rose, torn between disbelief, jealousy and amusement. 'Nothing at all?'

'Hmph. Well, nothing worth mentioning,' replied Joan darkly. 'Unless you count those loincloth things. What do they call them now? Bee stings? No, no, that's not it. B-strings?'

'I think you mean a G-string,' murmured Rose, struggling desperately not to laugh. 'A lot of people do sunbathe in those, you know.'

'Not in Polperro,' said Joan, quivering with indignation. 'We have our standards, I hope. And I don't like to see them flouted so shamelessly. The brazen young hussy even sat up and said good morning to me. I was so embarrassed I didn't know where to look, although I must say she was a very pretty girl and quite well spoken. All the same, I blame Greg for the whole disgraceful incident.'

'Perhaps he didn't know she was sunbathing topless in his garden,' ventured Rose.

Joan snorted. 'Then he should have done. She was his guest, wasn't she? Although what a man in his thirties was doing having a young girl like that staying overnight is more than I like to think about! Hugh Thomas tells me she came from a good family—ship owners, I believe—and he even had an idea there might be marriage in the air. But nothing came of it and Greg seems to have given her the brush-off now. Which just goes to show that he can't be trusted with women . . . now, will you have another cup of tea?'

Rose was silent, frowning thoughtfully as Joan bustled around the kitchen. She found the old woman's revelations mildly disquieting. Of course, there might be nothing in them, but after her own upsetting experience of Greg's charm and capacity for deceit it did make her feel distinctly uneasy. It was a relief to her when Joan plumped down at the table with a fresh pot of tea and changed the subject.

'Now, tell me, my love,' she said, 'have you heard from your mother?'

'Yes,' agreed Rose. 'I telephoned her when I was in Plymouth the other day. She's out of hospital and doing well and she should arrive in London in about two weeks' time, and, from what John Gleeson says, with luck we'll be able to move straight into the cottage. Would it be all right for me to stay here until then?'

'Stay as long as you like,' said Joan hospitably. 'I must say, it will be a real pleasure to see Fay again.'

Rose went to London two weeks later to meet her mother at Gatwick airport. All the way up on the train she brooded over her problem, a problem which hadn't been helped by the appearance every Friday evening of a fresh bunch of roses in the cottage, each time with a note attached saying simply, 'Forgive me'. There was never any sign of how they had arrived there and she never saw Greg leaving in a car, although she watched from behind the lace curtains in Joan's house. She suspected that John Gleeson was the courier, but she did not tackle him for fear of appearing ridiculous. Each time the flowers arrived all the familiar turmoil was reawakened. She couldn't bear to throw them away a second time, so she gave them to Joan and then had to endure the silent reproach of their exquisite perfume each time she entered the sitting-room, not to mention Joan's interested glances. But at least Rose always remained strong enough to resist contacting Greg. She knew that was what he was hoping for, she told herself that he would simply have to hope in vain. After all, he couldn't be in earnest with these apologies, could he? No. It was only a trick to lure her back so that he could have a casual fling with her. She told herself that macho pride prompted the flowers and the note, not affection. She must simply harden her heart and ignore him. But why was it so hard to do? As the train glided through the rolling green English countryside, why did she feel such a pang of misery at the mere thought that she was leaving Greg far behind? It was crazy, ridiculous, unworthy behaviour for a grown woman. She must stop behaving like a lovesick teenager and concentrate on welcoming her mother.

Fay Ashley's flight arrived at Gatwick only an hour late and she emerged into the arrivals lounge festooned with parcels. Rose felt a warm spurt of affection at the sight of that familiar figure looking like an older version of herself. Wavy brown hair streaked with grey, blue eyes, a round face with pink cheeks and a short, plump figure. That's how I'll look when I'm fifty-five, thought Rose, and smiled with a touch of wistfulness. Her mother was a lovely woman, but quite ordinary, just like Rose herself. Could someone as good-looking, rich and broodingly sensual as Greg Trelawney really be seriously interested in a girl without a shred of glamour? It didn't seem very likely! All the same, Rose thought defiantly as she ran forward to embrace her mother, ordinary people are often very nice...

'Oh, it is good to see you, my dear,' exclaimed Fay Ashley, dropping some of her parcels in a rather flustered way. 'All's well in Cornwall, then?'

'Everything's fine,' Rose reassured her. 'And how are you, Mum?'

'Tired, my love. It was a long flight, but I'm fully recovered from the operation.'

'That's good. I found a nice little bed-and-breakfast place in Hampstead. I thought we'd stay overnight there for a day or two until you feel fit to make the journey to Cornwall.'

Her mother smiled as she began gathering up her belongings. 'Well, I won't stay any longer than need be,' she said firmly. 'I can't wait to get home.'

It was worth all the trauma that Rose had been through since her arrival to see her mother's face as she got off the train in Looe. She looked at the steep green hills and the sapphire-blue sea with the gulls gliding overhead and burst into tears of joy.

'Oh, Rose. Oh, Rose.'

It was even better when they reached the cottage. John Gleeson had pulled out all the stops to finish work before Fay Ashley's arrival, and Rose felt a glow of pride as she showed her mother the refurbished kitchen, the handsome new bathrooms, the freshly plastered and papered walls and the thick new carpets.

'It's beautiful, my love,' exclaimed her mother. 'But it certainly wasn't like this when I left England thirty-five years ago. You must have done a lot of work on the place.'

'I did,' agreed Rose wryly.

Her mother's brows met in a worried frown. 'But how are we going to pay for it?' she asked.

'I took out a bank loan.'

'Can we afford it, Rose?'

'Don't worry! I'll make sure I pay back every penny of it. I'm writing some computer software at home and we should be able to start up our bed-and-breakfast business soon.'

'Won't we need council approval?' wondered her mother aloud.

'That's all organised,' said Rose. 'Now we only need to advertise in the newspapers, and I thought we could put our name down at the Looe tourist office.'

'How exciting! I wonder how long it will be before we get our first guest?'

They didn't have long to wait now that the builders had left. Rose felt a mingled sense of relief and disappointment at the realisation that she probably wouldn't receive her Friday evening bouquet. But she was wrong. Promptly at six o'clock on the Friday evening following her mother's arrival, there was a ring at the front doorbell.

'Who can that be?' demanded Fay. 'Joan always comes to the back door.'

Rose was just getting to her feet with a look of apprehension on her face when her mother walked briskly up the hall and flung open the front door.

'How odd!' she exclaimed. 'There's nobody here, but there's a beautiful bunch of flowers on the front step. Look, Rose. And there's a note with them.'

Rose practically elbowed her mother out of the way as she dived around her to snatch the bouquet. 'Damn him!' she muttered under her breath. 'Why won't he leave me alone?' Picking up the roses, she flung them furiously down the front steps. A note fluttered free and lay pathetically at her feet, its writing clearly visible. 'Forgive me'.

'What's this all about?' demanded her mother with a look that was half worried, half fascinated.

'Look, Mum, I don't mean to be rude,' snapped Rose, 'but would you please *mind your own business*?'

Then, with a choking groan, Rose pushed past her mother, ran up the stairs and slammed her bedroom door. She was still sitting moodily with her head in her hands and a stormy expression on her face when her mother arrived ten minutes later with a cup of tea. She set it down on Rose's bedside chest and sat on the end of the bed, eyeing her daughter thoughtfully.

'Oh, my love,' she murmured, putting her hand on Rose's knee. 'Don't take on like that. What's it all about? Is that dreadful Martin Inglis still pestering you? Did he send the roses?'

'Martin?' echoed Rose as if she had never heard the name before in her life. 'Oh, Martin! No, it wasn't him.'

'Then who?' demanded her mother, looking intrigued.

'Don't ask!' flared Rose.

Shaking her head, Far Ashley wisely left the room without saying any more. But the next morning she woke Rose up at seven-thirty with a brisk knock on her door. Her eyes were shining as she came into Rose's bedroom.

'Guess what?' she demanded. 'We've got our first booking, Rose.'

'Oh, who is it?' asked Rose without interest.

'I didn't quite catch the name, the woman rang off too fast. She was a Ms Helen Arbuthnot ringing up to book a room for her brother. Apparently he's rather run down and suffering from depression, poor man. I gather he's gone through some kind of personal crisis, perhaps a broken marriage? Anyway, he wants somewhere quiet to get away from it all and if he likes it he'll be coming back a lot in the future. Isn't that exciting?'

'Mm.'

'Oh, come on, Rose! It's exactly what we wanted. Anyway, he's arriving tomorrow morning and I'm counting on you to help me. Now promise me you'll stop moping and give him a really good welcome. All right?'

'All right,' agreed Rose listlessly.

But when Helen Arbuthnot's brother arrived the following morning Rose was goaded out of her listlessness. They both heard the sound of a car pulling up in the driveway and the peal of the front doorbell, then Fay gave Rose a gentle push. 'Go on, you answer it, my love. It'll be nicer for him to see someone young and pretty.'

Rose opened the door, determined to make polite conversation, but what she saw drove all thoughts of politeness out of her mind. There was a Rolls-Royce parked in the driveway and a tall, muscular man with brooding, dark eyes planted ominously on the doorstep. Rose reeled back as if she'd been shot.

'You!' she breathed.

'Hello, Rose,' murmured Greg.

CHAPTER SIX

FOR a moment Rose was so startled that her mouth fell open and she retreated a pace or two down the hallway. This gave Greg the opportunity to step confidently inside. Part of Rose's brain registered that he was expensively dressed in lightweight, pleated beige trousers, a striped open-necked shirt and a tan suede jacket with a zipped front and ribbed cuffs, and that he carried a glossy Louis Vuitton suitcase in his left hand. Then her mind reeled away from these trivial details to a far more pressing problem.

'Why can't you leave me alone?' she hissed.

'Because I want to see you,' said Greg in an injured voice.

'Well, I don't want to see you! Go away!'

His heavy black eyebrows arched mockingly and a small, taunting smile played about the corners of his lips. 'Oh, come, now,' he murmured. 'What's your mother going to say if you turn away a perfectly good paying guest?'

Rose ground her teeth, uttered a strangled sound and was just about to launch into a blistering retort when her mother suddenly appeared in the hallway behind her. Fay Ashley came forward with her face wreathed in smiles and both hands outstretched.

'Good morning, Mr...'

'Trelawney. Greg Trelawney.'

Fay's face lit up with interest. 'Welcome to Rose Cottage. I'm Fay Ashley and this is my daughter, Rose. Trelawney... Now, that rings a bell. I remember a Pauline

110

Trelawney in Polperro, many years ago. She was married to a fisherman. Would she be any relation of yours?'

'She's my mother,' agreed Greg.

'How nice!' exclaimed Fay. 'Perhaps I could go and call on her some time.'

'I'm afraid you'll have to wait until Christmas, then,' said Greg with an engaging smile. 'She lives in Florida now, you know.'

'I thought you said she lived on the Atlantic coast!' burst out Rose, unable to contain her indignation.

'Florida's on the Atlantic coast,' pointed out Greg.

'Well, you certainly haven't wasted any time making friends, have you, Rose?' asked her mother brightly. 'I can see you've been having a nice little chat already. Do come in, Mr Trelawney, and let me hang up your jacket and show you your room. Then perhaps you'd like a nice cup of tea. I'll pop into the kitchen and make it in a moment. I'm sure my daughter Rose will keep you company and give you anything else you want.'

'Oh, I'm sure she will too,' agreed Greg in a velvety voice, casting Rose a provocative sideways glance.

Not trusting herself to remain silent another moment, Rose muttered something incoherent and fled to the sitting-room. When Fay had hung up Greg's jacket, shown him his room and disappeared into the kitchen, he came in search of Rose in the sitting-room. She whirled around at the sound of his footsteps and cast him a glance full of loathing.

'You can't do this to me, Greg!' she protested hotly.

'Why not?' he asked in a steely voice. 'You chose to ignore my apologies when I sent them by letter, so I thought it was time I delivered them in person.'

'Oh, so you've come to apologise, have you?' sneered Rose.

'Yes.'

'All right,' said Rose with a toss of her head. 'Your apology is accepted. Now please go.'

Greg strode across the room and made himself comfortable in front of the fireplace with one arm leaning negligently on the mantelpiece. His dark eyes scanned her face searchingly with the shrewd, inquisitorial look that she had come to dread.

'No,' he murmured in a voice that was all the more alarming for its Cornish softness. 'I won't go. At least, not until we've had this matter out.'

'Why not?'

'Because my apology is not really accepted unless you wipe out the offence and go back to where we were.'

'With you filling me full of lies and trying to make a fool of me?' challenged Rose.

Greg's mouth tightened. 'I had no intention of making a fool of you.'

'Well, what did you intend to do?' snapped Rose.

'I never had a calculated plan of action,' he snapped back. 'I'm not like that, I never have been. I just see what I want and go for it. And I wanted you, Rose. I still do.'

The way he looked at her sent a thrill of mingled excitement and misgiving down her spine. She turned away, her breast heaving, trying to fight down the turmoil of attraction and resentment that seemed to be setting every nerve in her body on fire.

'Well, I don't want you!'

'You're lying!' growled Greg, and with a swift movement he crossed the room and took her in his arms.

Her heart fluttered like a frightened bird and her breath came in shallow gulps as she looked up into his stormy face. What might have happened next she never found out, for at that moment they heard the rattle of the tea-trolley in the hall and Greg released her. The air seemed to vibrate with tension as Fay entered the room, but Rose was determined to hide her feelings. It would be too embarrassing to endure if her mother found out the truth about her and Greg, so she concealed her confusion under a light, bright manner.

'Do sit down and have some tea, Mr Trelawney,' she invited sweetly.

'Greg, please.'

'Greg,' Rose corrected herself, glaring at him over her mother's shoulder. 'Tell me, how would you like your tea?'

'Black, please, no sugar.'

Fay made herself comfortable in one of the newly re-upholstered armchairs and pushed the tea-tray invitingly towards Greg.

'You will try some of Rose's scones, won't you? She's an excellent cook.'

'Really?' asked Greg with polite interest. 'Then I look forward to sampling some of her other offerings. Perhaps you'll make me a Cornish speciality for lunch, Miss Ashley?'

'Oh, call her Rose,' urged her mother. 'We're all friends here, aren't we? And my name's Fay.'

While Rose sat seething over her tea and scones, Greg drew her mother into conversation about her recent journey and her life in Australia. If she hadn't been so furious with him, Rose would have admired his pleasant manners. At last her mother gathered up the empty cups and plates and smiled at Greg.

'Now, make yourself at home,' she urged. 'We generally eat lunch about one o'clock, if that suits you, and you can either eat alone or with us, whichever you prefer. And just do as you please for the rest of the morning. There's a very nice walk along the beach, or you might prefer to go for a drive.'

'Yes, I might,' agreed Greg thoughtfully. 'Perhaps I could persuade you to come with me ... Rose?'

'I don't think so...Greg. I'll be too busy whipping up something special for your lunch.'

Later, when Rose was in the kitchen making pastry, her mother came in and leaned against one of the counters with a second cup of tea.

'He's very nice, isn't he?' she demanded enthusiastically. 'So handsome and so charming. But there seems to be something rather melancholy just below the surface. I wonder if he really has had a broken marriage? I can't help feeling that some woman has treated him very badly, poor man.'

'Not badly enough,' muttered Rose beneath the whirr of the food processor.

'What did you say, my love?'

'Nothing, nothing.'

'Well, if you've got everything under control here, Rose, I might just pop out into the garden for a while.'

Once Fay had disappeared into the garden, Rose was left to fume in peace. Try as she might, she could think of no satisfactory way of getting rid of Greg. She certainly had no intention of telling her mother the truth and, without doing so, there was no way of revealing him as anything other than an impeccable paying guest. Yet the prospect of spending an entire weekend or even longer having to dance attendance on him filled her with silent rage. How dared he gatecrash her home like this and sit there with that gloating smile, revelling in every moment of her humiliation as she poured his tea and passed his scones? She'd like to slap his smirking face! She could almost feel the stinging impact of her palm against his cheek, see the stormy narrowing of his eyes and the way he would catch her hand. Then he'd glare down at her with an expression that made her breath come faster...and she would laugh in his face. That would infuriate him! He'd probably turn her hand over and drop a lingering kiss on her flesh, then back her into

a corner and... With a muffled groan, Rose slammed
a large wad of pastry down on the board and attacked
it viciously with a rolling pin.

Fay had set the table in the dining-room with a lace
tablecloth and a bunch of daisies in a blue and white
jug. With the sunlight streaming in the window through
the new blue and white floral chintz curtains, it all looked
fresh and charming and Rose felt a pang of regret that
this could not be a genuinely friendly lunch. All the same,
a sense of unholy amusement gripped her at the expression on Greg's face when she carried in the pie,
golden brown and crisp from the oven. A magnificent
pie, except for the half-dozen fishes' heads which poked
mournfully up through the centre of the crust.

'What's this?' asked Greg apprehensively.

Rose smiled with gentle malice. 'Star-gazy pie,' she
purred. 'It's a great favourite in Cornwall, so I'm told,
especially among the old-fashioned fishermen.'

'Yes, but Rose,' protested her mother, 'you've never
left the fish heads on in the past when you've made it.
They've always been decently covered before. I'm afraid
you'll put Greg off his food.'

'Oh, I don't think so,' murmured Rose. 'It takes a lot
to put Greg off anything he wants. Anyway, as I understand it, he's very fond of living like an old-fashioned,
traditional fisherman.'

Fay cast a puzzled glance from one to the other as if
she was not quite certain what was going on. Then, to
Rose's alarm, Greg suddenly carried the war into her
camp. His lean brown fingers closed gently over her hand
and he smiled suavely.

'I think it's time we let your mother in on our little
secret, don't you, Rose? Fay, I'm sure you must have
guessed by now that Rose and I aren't meeting for the
first time. We've actually become very close friends since

she's been here at Pisky Bay. Perhaps you'd like me to
tell your mother how close, Rose?'

Rose's blue eyes danced with rage and she gave Greg
a sharp warning kick under the table.

His smile wavered fractionally and his grip on her hand
tightened.

'Well, perhaps not,' he continued smoothly. 'But if
you don't feel like sitting here reminiscing over the fun
we've had together in the last month, would you like to
come for a drive with me this afternoon instead?'

Rose held her breath and counted to ten. It was all
she could do to stop herself leaping to her feet and
dumping the pie, fish heads and all, on top of Greg's
glossy black hair. The hide of the man! It was barefaced
blackmail! If she didn't agree, he was obviously going
to start releasing titbits of information to her mother
until he finally had Rose writhing and squirming and
begging for mercy. The brute!

'That would be nice, Greg,' she cooed. 'I can hardly
wait. After all, even though we've already had several
interesting little chats, there's still a lot I'd like to say to
you.'

'I thought there might be,' muttered Greg with a glint
in his eye. Tranquilly he released his grip on her hand.
'Well, if you'll excuse us after lunch, Fay, I think Rose
and I might take a little jaunt to Fowey for the afternoon.
Now I must try some of this . . . delicious-looking pie.'

In spite of its intimidating appearance, the pie was
actually very good, filled with filleted fish, chopped
onion, eggs and herbs. With minted new potatoes and
runner beans from Joan Penwithick's garden it made an
excellent meal. Greg and Fay followed it up with rasp-
berries and fresh cream, but Rose had unaccountably
lost her appetite.

Her feelings were in turmoil as the Rolls-Royce glided
smoothly through the leafy green countryside an hour

later. She sat stiffly upright, casting Greg occasional wary, hostile glances and feeling far too apprehensive to relax in the cushioned softness of the leather upholstery. What did he want from her now? Was he planning to renew his pursuit of her? Or did his pride simply insist on having the last word in their exchange of fire? Yet although she would have hotly denied it, Rose's feelings were not entirely negative. She could not help being intrigued and somewhat flattered by Greg's relentless pursuit of her. Added to that, there was no doubt that he still exuded the same dangerous animal magnetism. She would have to be very careful to keep her wits about her in this encounter! At last Greg turned off into a hedge-lined lane which came out into an open space on top of a cliff.

'Would you like to get out and stretch your legs?' he invited.

Rose glared at him suspiciously. 'I thought we were going to Fowey?'

'We are, but we have a few things to say to each other first and I thought they were better said in private.'

Flashing him a stormy look, Rose climbed out of the car, folded her arms aggressively and leaned back against the bonnet to try to control the faint tremor in her legs.

'Well, go on,' she urged.

Greg looked amused. He too had left the car and was now standing facing her with his hands negligently on his hips and the dazzling blue backdrop of the ocean behind him.

'Your turn first,' he invited.

'I have nothing to say,' snapped Rose frostily. 'Except perhaps this. Why did you come and stay in our cottage and then blackmail me into coming out here with you?'

Greg shrugged. 'All's fair in love and war.'

'And which is this?' she demanded tartly.

'Both,' he said with a steely undertone in his voice.

Rose gave a mirthless gasp of laughter. 'And you hold all the cards, don't you? You think you can bully me into doing whatever you like just with the unspoken threat of embarrassing me in front of my mother.'

Greg's face suddenly looked stern. 'I would never do that,' he vowed. 'And you can believe what you like, Rose, but I'm telling you the truth now. All I want is to talk to you, really talk, and if you don't want to see me after today, I swear I won't trouble you again.'

'What do you want to talk about?' demanded Rose in a voice that was fractionally less hostile.

'I just want to hear the truth about your feelings towards me.'

'You won't like it!'

Greg winced. 'I suppose I deserve that. All right, now that you've had time to cool off, what do you feel about me?'

'I despise you.'

'So you're still smoldering with resentment,' said Greg, nodding shrewdly. 'Can you tell me why?'

'Because you made a fool of me!' flared Rose. 'You let me think you were genuinely attracted to me and all the time it was just a game to you. You treated me without the slightest scrap of respect.'

Greg shook his head and sighed. 'I'm sorry. I can only repeat what I've already said to you. I didn't intend to make a fool of you and I was genuinely attracted to you. All the same, I admit that I went too far and I obviously offended you deeply.'

'Then why did you do it?' burst out Rose.

'Because I couldn't resist you. When I saw you sitting there in my boat in that awful policewoman's skirt and white blouse with your face glowing and your hair flowing in the wind, you seemed like a complete mass of contradictions. You were determined to come across as brisk and efficient and hard as nails, yet you had those

amazing little dimples when you smiled and there was
something stormy and passionate at the backs of your
eyes. It intrigued me. Besides, you were so desperately
proper, so tense and suspicious when I tried to show you
how to take the wheel that I couldn't help suspecting
that you'd recently been hurt by a man and hurt badly.
I wanted to know who he was and whether you were
now a free woman. There were all kinds of things I
wanted to know about you! That's why I came ashore
at Pisky Bay intending to stay overnight. It didn't seem
wrong to me at the time. I thought I'd see you safely
settled in the cottage and I certainly didn't intend to do
you any harm.'

'But you kissed me!' protested Rose.

Greg gave a wry smile. 'That wasn't part of my plan.
It just happened.'

'Oh, yes?'

'Well, I won't pretend I'm sorry for that,' retorted
Greg defiantly. 'Are you?'

A fleeting range of expressions chased across Rose's
face at the memory of that kiss. She felt again the
warmth, the excitement, the feeling of drowning in delicious sensual abandon as Greg hauled her into that
savage embrace. Then she remembered the lies he had
told her and the light in her eyes was suddenly quenched.

'Yes!' she blazed. 'I am sorry.'

'Tell me the truth,' insisted Greg.

'It is the truth! I wish I'd never met you.'

'Yet that first night you liked me, didn't you?' he demanded. 'You were attracted to me. The truth, mind.'

Rose's face flushed. 'I suppose so,' she muttered
ungraciously.

'Then why is it so different now?'

'Because you lied to me!' she shouted. 'You spoiled
everything between us.'

'But supposing I had told you the truth right then, that I was a rich man with millions of pounds' worth of assets, what would you have done?'

Rose's eyes flickered away over the heaving blue sea as she wrestled with that question. What would she have done if Greg had told her he was rich? Run a mile probably. The thought evidently showed in her face, for Greg's lips twisted in a triumphant smile.

'Exactly,' he said drily.

'I didn't say anything.'

'You didn't need to. It was written in your face. In any case, you told me pretty plainly that night that you didn't think you could ever trust another man again, especially a rich one. What was I supposed to do?'

'You should have given up and gone away. You should have avoided causing me any more pain.' Yet even as she said it Rose felt an obscure pang because she knew that wasn't what she wanted. If Greg had left her that night and never come back, she would have felt a perverse sense of disappointment. So what did she want?

'Given up?' echoed Greg in disgust. 'I would never have been so gutless!'

'Don't twist things to make it seem as if you're right!' exclaimed Rose. 'If you wanted to get to know me you could have done it decently, gone through the proper channels. You should have told me who you really were and let me choose for myself whether I wanted anything more to do with you.'

'Perhaps,' retorted Greg doubtfully. 'But I've come to realise over the last ten years or so that having money is a two-edged sword. A lot of women are intimidated by it, others are attracted for all the wrong reasons. If my money was going to be a barrier between us, I didn't want you to know about it. What I wanted was for you to react to me simply as a woman to a man. On that level I think you and I were pure dynamite together.'

'No, we weren't!' protested Rose, averting her gaze from his dark, compelling eyes. All the old antagonism and attraction seemed to be back in full measure.

'Who are you trying to convince?' he demanded contemptuously. 'Yourself or me?'

Rose darted a swift, tormented look at him. She thought of Joan and her description of the 'goings on' at Greg's cottage, of Hugh and his accusations about the mysterious Ingrid, and an acute pain lanced through her. For a moment she was tempted to demand an explanation from him, but pride restrained her. It would be too humiliating if she let him see how deeply he had the power to hurt her. And, in any case, he might just come out with another glib lie. Better to deny everything.

'There's no question of convincing anyone,' she replied as coolly as if she were giving a lecture on computer science. 'I simply think you're exaggerating. I don't recall any "dynamite" between us.'

Greg looked at her with an expression of intense scorn. Then suddenly he hauled her into his arms and kissed her so brutally and hungrily that the landscape swirled dizzily around her and her heart hammered unevenly in her breast.

'Does that refresh your memory?' he demanded at last, when they both came up for air.

'I hate you!' she breathed.

An odd, forced smile touched his lips. 'That's better than pretending you're indifferent to me. When can I see you again, Rose?'

'Never,' she replied unsteadily.

'Are you really too much of a coward even to spend time with me?'

'I'm not a coward!' she retorted, stung by the insult.

'Then have lunch with me tomorrow. Live adventurously. Find out if you want me as a lover and to hell with whether I'm rich and dangerous or poor and safe.'

'No!' cried Rose in a tormented voice. 'It's crazy. I don't want to risk it.'

Greg glared at her for a moment, his face alight with scorn and a vibrant, hungry longing that sent thrills of panic and excitement chasing down her spine. Then he turned contemptuously away and strode towards the car.

'In that case, there's nothing else to be said, is there?' he demanded. 'Get in and I'll drive you home. There's no need for you ever to see me again.'

Could he really be intending to walk out of her life as simply as that with all this unresolved conflict and need seething between them? Rose stared after him in dismay and suddenly realised that she couldn't bear to let him go. It might be insanity, but...

'Greg, wait!' she cried impetuously, running after him and seizing his arm.

'What is it?' he growled.

'You don't don't have to walk right out of my life!' she gabbled. 'Polperro's a small place; we're bound to keep seeing each other. Can't we be... friends?'

'Friends?' He tried the word on his tongue as if it had a bitter taste. Then he looked down at her with an intensity that alarmed her. 'I don't want to be your friend, Rose, but it will do as a beginning. Why don't we start by having lunch at my boatyard in Plymouth tomorrow?'

They set out for Plymouth shortly after ten the following morning. At nine-thirty, Rose was still lingering indecisively in front of her mirror, with half her clothes discarded on the bed. Then she heard a light tap at the door. Was it Greg? Did she look all right? She cast a hasty, dissatisfied glance at her pale blue suit and white blouse.

'Come in.'

But it wasn't Greg, it was her mother.

'I've ironed your best striped blouse, Rose. I thought you might need it.'

'Thanks, Mum. You're a genius.'

She put the fresh blouse on and turned sideways to inspect herself. In the mirror she saw her mother hovering behind her with an expression of barely suppressed curiosity and concern on her face. Rose felt a rush of exasperation. Couldn't she have any kind of private life at all?

'I suppose you want to know why I'm running off with our first paying guest,' she demanded in a resigned voice.

'Oh, Rose, I didn't say a word! But I can't help feeling rather worried. Joan Penwithick said——'

'I might have known Joan would have something to say. The two of you were crouched over your teacups like a pair of fortune-tellers when we came in last night. Anyway, what did she say?'

Fay sat on the bed and her voice took on a hushed and rather melodramatic tone. 'I know Greg is very handsome in a surly sort of way and he can be extremely charming. But there's something so...so lawless about him. I'm not sure that I altogether trust him to treat you with respect, dear. And then there's his reputation. Joan says he's been involved with any number of women and there was one Danish girl who——'

'That's all just gossip!' broke in Rose impatiently. 'If I don't care about it, I don't see why you should.' She fought down the uneasy feeling that she did care and began brushing her hair with long, vicious strokes. 'Don't make such a fuss, Mum. I'm old enough to take care of myself.'

Fay sighed. 'I suppose so,' she murmured without conviction. Then her face brightened. 'Of course, it will stop you brooding over Martin.'

'I'm not brooding over Martin!'

'And Greg has made a great success of his business, that's another thing to consider. Any woman who marries him could be sure of an extremely comfortable life.'

'Mum! I wouldn't marry someone just to have a comfortable life.'

'No, dear, no. But it does help.'

'Look, Mum, I'm not planning to get married today anyway. Greg and I are just friends. Do you understand? Friends! There is nothing more between us.'

I wish that were true, thought Rose moodily as they flashed through lush green countryside an hour later. If only my heart didn't beat faster every time I looked at Greg, life could be much simpler. But he doesn't look as if he's suffering too much! Greg caught her gaze, smiled blandly at her and began to whistle softly under his breath as he turned his attention back to the road. Watching him closely, Rose found it hard to believe that such passionate emotions had ever ignited between them. Had he really held her half naked in his arms and murmured hoarse words of endearment to her? It seemed impossible! But if he had, if the whole tempestuous drama they had been through together was solid fact and not a wild flight of her imagination, then how could Greg put it behind him so easily? How could he accept a lukewarm friendship in place of passion without even a flicker of regret? The only possible explanation was that he hadn't cared much in the beginning. While Rose had experienced feelings that had stirred her to the depths of her soul, Greg had obviously just been playing an amusing little game with her. Or had he? She mustn't be too hasty in judging. Perhaps when she saw him at work, surrounded by people who knew a different facet of him, she would have a better understanding of his enigmatic character...

When they reached Plymouth, Greg drove to an imposing two-storey villa, set on a hillside with a swooping view of the harbour. Rose's eyes widened as a pair of huge wrought-iron gates swung open at the touch of a button and the Rolls glided up a gravel driveway between neatly manicured hedges.

'Come in and have a cup of coffee,' invited Greg, parking the car in a sweeping turning circle in front of the main entrance. 'I have to pick up a few files in any case, so we may as well freshen up before we go to the shipyard.'

He opened the front door and ushered Rose into an entrance hall that took her breath away. The house was relatively modern, dating perhaps to the nineteen-fifties, and the architect and decorator had made maximum possible use of light and water. In front of Rose was a vast atrium, soaring to the full height of the house and lit by a glass roof. The walls on either side were faced with a peach-coloured marble and down one of them a massive artificial waterfall rippled behind a sheet of frosted glass. Invitingly deep cream leather sofas were scattered around in groups, flanked by green palms. The whole effect was one of dramatic visual splendour, counterpointed by a practical regard for comfort.

'I-it's beautiful,' stammered Rose.

'Thank you. I got the idea from a house I own near our Hong Kong branch.'

'Hong Kong? You have a branch in Hong Kong?'

'Yes,' agreed Greg, tossing his jacket carelessly on one of the sofas. 'I have branches in every continent except Antarctica now and I can't bear hotels, so I always make sure that I have my own house to stay in while I'm abroad.'

Rose was still digesting that fact when a grey-haired woman in a floral pinafore emerged into the entrance hall and gave a faint, reproachful sigh.

'Oh, Mr Trelawney, and with a guest, too! I'm sorry, sir, I've just mopped the kitchen and the downstairs bathrooms. You should have told me you were coming.'

'Don't worry, Agnes, we won't walk on your wet floors. We'll go into the conservatory and perhaps you could bring us some coffee there in a moment. By the way, this is Miss Rose Ashley. Agnes Parker, my housekeeper.'

The greetings over, Greg led Rose to a magnificent conservatory overlooking the harbour. 'I'm sorry about that,' he said. 'You'd better not risk breaking your neck in the downstairs bathrooms, so you can use the one off my bedroom.'

He led her upstairs to a luxurious suite of rooms, papered in gold and white embossed wallpaper with thick carpets, French Empire furniture and a vast carved bed. Opening a door, he revealed a bathroom lined with topaz-coloured marble and gleaming with mirrors and gold fittings.

'Help yourself to anything you need,' he instructed. 'And just come down when you're ready.'

Rose was so enchanted by this extravaganza of a bathroom that she lingered to explore the top of the washstand and discovered twin speakers and an array of switches concealed in the mahogany surrounds. Curiously she touched one of the switches. Ballet music sprang into the air. And another switch. Reggae. She reached for the volume control and gasped as a splinter of mahogany suddenly drove deep under her nail.

'Ow, ow, ow! Why couldn't I leave things alone?'

Pulling open the mirrored bathroom cabinet, she searched frantically for tweezers. There were three sliding doors and, while the first two opened easily, the third one jammed. As Rose tugged it free, a prescription form and a slip of paper fluttered on to the washstand, then she found what she was looking for. Thirty painful seconds, a squeeze of antiseptic cream and one Band-Aid later and the disaster was over. She began to tidy up. The Band-Aid wrapper went into the bin, the cream and tweezers into the cabinet, the prescription form had only to be wiped dry... without any conscious will on her part, the words leapt into her brain: 'Miss Ingrid Jensen. Microgynon.'

What on earth was a pharmaceutical prescription with a woman's name on it doing in Greg's bathroom? Well, it was none of Rose's business. She picked up the slip of paper which had fallen with it and began to put it back in the prescription cover. As she did so, she could not help seeing the words printed at the top. There was an address of a Plymouth doctor's surgery and a list of advice, beginning, 'If this is your first experience of taking birth-control pills, you may find that...'

Rose caught her breath and looked hastily away, feeling suddenly so sick and shaken that she had to hold on to the top of the washstand. Oh, no! She hadn't meant to pry, it had been purely an accident... but what on earth was a prescription for the Pill doing in Greg's bathroom? And who was Ingrid—surely not just 'Nobody important... a girl who works for me' as Greg had told Rose? Hugh Thomas had accused Greg of taking advantage of her, but Greg had denied it. Well, he would, wouldn't he? thought Rose with a sudden spurt of anger. He'd tell any lie that suited him to get him out of trouble. But it would be hard to find a lie that would cover this. Hard to think of any explanation except the obvious one. That Greg was either having an affair with this girl right now, or had been doing so until recently. Rose looked at the date on the prescription. It was barely three months old, repeats would still be valid... A low groan escaped her. Poor girl! Had she been deceived by Greg just as thoroughly as Rose had? And what was the best thing to do now? Should she put the form back and act as if nothing had happened? After all, she felt like a snoop for discovering it, even though it had been an accident. And yet she couldn't just go on as if nothing had happened. Or should she tackle him? Demand an explanation? But what right did she have to do that? After all, she wasn't Greg's wife, or even his steady girlfriend. Just his...friend. And at the moment she felt friendly enough to sentence him to a firing squad. He's not worth worrying about if he's so fickle and deceitful, she told herself sternly. But then why did she feel this corrosive jealousy, this gnawing, irrational pain at the thought that he might even now be sleeping with another woman?

Reason told her that she should put the form back, should stay out of something that didn't concern her. It was an embarrassing situation and would be made no better if she meddled in it. Yet some impulse too powerful to resist drew her fingers back to that rectangle of white paper. Holding it gingerly as if it were radio-active, she slipped it into the pocket of her jacket. What do you think you're going to do with it? she asked herself in exasperation. You've never been the interfering type. You should stay out of this. But good sense no longer had the power to sway her. I don't care! she thought defiantly. Sensible or not, I'm going to ask Greg about this.

She came hurrying impetuously down the marble staircase and almost collided with Greg, who was halfway up. The sight of him made her come to a halt, her breast heaving and her eyes stormy. How could he look so normal, so calm and mocking and relaxed, when his be-haviour was causing her such heartache?

'What's wrong?' he asked. 'You look upset. You haven't hurt yourself, have you?' His gaze went to the sticking plaster on her finger.

'Oh, that,' she said unsteadily. 'I got a splinter under my fingernail upstairs.'

His face was full of concern. 'Was it serious?'

'No.' She paused, drawing in breath, trying to frame the words, I found this upstairs. Can you explain what it was doing there? But her nerve failed her. Instead of voicing her doubts and suspicions, she stood scanning Greg's face with an anguished, searching gaze.

'Well, that's good,' he murmured with a puzzled frown. 'Why don't you come down and have some coffee, then?'

He turned to lead the way and Rose found her voice.

'Greg!' she blurted out. 'Who's Ingrid Jensen really?'

He stopped as if he had just been struck by a knife between the shoulder blades and his grip on the marble balustrade stiffened. Then he turned with elaborate casualness and gave Rose a faint, careless smile that set alarm bells clamouring in her brain.

'A spoilt brat who's been sent over from Denmark to learn about administering shipyards.' He turned away again as if he had told her everything she needed to know. Rose's voice rang out, sharp and desperate, calling him back.

'Yes, but what's she like, Greg? And what sort of dealings do you have with her?'

'What's she like?' repeated Greg with a stormy expression on his face. 'Words fail me when it comes to describing Ingrid. She's nineteen and wants her own way in everything. At first I found her extremely appealing but now I avoid her like the plague. She's very rich, very beautiful, very tiresome. The kind of woman who could easily drive a man insane.'

'Oh,' said Rose in a small voice. 'But did you...was she...Greg, have you been having an affair with her?'

There was no mistaking the blaze of annoyance in Greg's dark eyes. An annoyance that was followed immediately by a shuttered, defensive look as if he were preparing to withstand a siege. 'No,' he muttered, but he would not meet her gaze. 'And I'll thank you not to ask me any further questions about the matter. Now, come and drink your coffee and then we'll leave.'

Rose would have been impressed by the shipyard with its massive dry-docks where huge commercial vessels were under construction if she hadn't been in such a state of turmoil. As it was, she couldn't take in a quarter of what she was being shown. Like a laboratory rat on a treadmill, she kept running over and over the same ground. Greg had lied to her about his occupation, so wasn't it likely that he was lying about his dealings with Ingrid too? Rose shouldn't even want him for a friend, much less a lover. He was despicable, wasn't he? So why did she keep craving his company as urgently as if he were some kind of addictive drug? Why did she still feel this treacherous yearning to stay with him, to ignore her doubts? What she really ought to do was storm away from this place in protest. Instead, with an increasingly heavy heart, she allowed Greg to guide her around the shipyard and, at one o'clock, to take her off for lunch in the boardroom. This was a serene retreat featuring eggshell-blue walls hung with Chinese paintings complemented by a magnificent black lacquered dining-table and matching chairs. Not that the meal could be called a success. They sat glowering at each other and exchanging little more than common civilities as they worked their way through spicy crumbed shrimps with a green salad and white wine. They had just embarked on lemon water ices when there was an assertive knock at the boardroom door.

'Come in!' called Greg.

A tall, striking blonde girl with flawless features, a deep tan and a curvaceous figure emphasised by a skin-tight black dress undulated into the room and gazed soulfully at the pair of them. Greg's face took on a haunted expression.

'What do you want, Ingrid?' he demanded sharply.

Dark black eyes, studying him, his mouth and again
severely at the pair of them. Greg's face took on a
hunted expression.

'What do you want, Greg?' he demanded sharply.

CHAPTER SEVEN

THE girl stared back at Greg with a stricken expression
in her limpid blue eyes. For an instant she looked rather
like a scolded child with her full lower lip stuck out and
her forehead wrinkled as if she was about to cry. Yet
there was nothing childlike about either her figure or her
clothing. She was a good six inches taller than Rose and
her dress had obviously come from one of the top
couturiers of Europe. Made of clinging crêpe de Chine,
it was cut with deceptive simplicity to show off her high
bust, tiny waist and long, shapely legs. She wore a
minimum of jewellery—gold and pearl earrings, a gold
necklace and gold watch—and her straight hair fell in a
shiny flaxen curtain around her shoulders. She was ten
thousand times more glamorous than Rose would ever
be and yet there was something terribly vulnerable in her
manner.

'What do you want, Ingrid?' repeated Greg.

Ingrid pouted a little at his tone, but continued to gaze
wistfully at him. 'I just came in to tell you that an important fax has arrived from Copenhagen. The *Helga
Pedersen* has been delivered safely and sea trials will
begin next week.'

'That's good news,' said Greg more mildly. 'But it
was hardly necessary to interrupt our lunch to tell me,
Ingrid. Off you go, now. Miss Ashley and I are busy.'

'Oh, are you a client?' asked Ingrid eagerly, turning
to Rose. Something in her manner had an odd pathos,
as if she hoped desperately that Rose would turn out to
be only a customer and therefore not a threat to her.

'No, I——' began Rose.

'Miss Ashley is my friend, Ingrid,' said Greg firmly. 'My very close friend. She has been staying at my cottage in Polperro and I hope she'll soon spend some time here in Plymouth with me.'

Ingrid's response was startling. The cornflower-blue eyes immediately flooded with tears, the pouting lips opened and closed twice, then she flashed Rose a burning look, gave a muffled gasp and ran from the room.

'Why on earth did you tell her that?' demanded Rose in exasperation, rising to her feet.

'Women!' exclaimed Greg, rolling his eyes despairingly.

Flinging down her napkin, Rose hurried in pursuit of the younger girl. An odd maelstrom of emotions was seething through her as she strode down the corridor. Bewilderment, indignation, compassion and just a pinch of curiosity. Fortunately the noise Ingrid was emitting made the hunt an easy one. In a very short time Rose ran her to earth in a tea-room overlooking the shipyard. Curled up in a chair, with her face buried in her hands, the Danish girl was sobbing with the wholehearted abandon of a child having a tantrum. As Rose entered the room she sat up with a jerk, uncovering her face to reveal red, swollen eyes and quivering lips. Taking in the situation, Rose crossed to the sink, tore off a strip of kitchen paper from the dispenser and handed it to the girl.

'What's wrong?' she asked sympathetically as Ingrid dabbed at her eyes and nose.

'E-everything.'

'Oh, come on!' urged Rose, swallowing a smile. 'It can't be that bad.'

'It is! It is! I'm so much in love with Greg and now you're trying to take him away from me.'

That unsettled Rose. Perhaps Ingrid had genuine grounds for putting on an emotional display. All the same, Rose recalled Greg's exasperated denial of any wrongdoing earlier in the day and tried to keep her voice calm and soothing as she replied. 'How can anyone take Greg away from you if he's not really yours?'

'But he was! He was! We were living together...he loved me, he told me he did.'

A pain like a knife blade went through Rose's entire body at this outburst. Somehow there was a nightmare realism about Ingrid's assertions. Almost against her will, Rose's hand travelled to her pocket and drew out the prescription form.

'Did you leave this at Greg's house?' she asked.

Ingrid accepted the paper with a puzzled look and scrutinised it swiftly. Then a blaze of excitement suddenly lit her eyes. 'Yes, yes! This proves what I was telling you. I lived with Greg when I first came here from Denmark. We fell in love and started sleeping together. But then a few months ago we had a big quarrel and he made me leave and live somewhere else. He was so cruel that I wanted to die.'

'Don't be ridiculous,' protested Rose. 'You're a very silly girl to talk like that, and if you were sleeping with Greg it was very unwise of you. You're far too young to know your own mind yet about things like that. You should be getting on with learning your job and enjoying yourself.'

Ingrid snorted. 'You sound just like Greg,' she cried with a flash of temper. 'He was always preaching at me too.'

'And yet you say he had an affair with you?' demanded Rose shrewdly.

Ingrid flushed. 'Yes!' she insisted. 'I suppose he thought it was all right because everyone was expecting us to get married.'

'What do you mean?' demanded Rose. 'Why did everyone expect you to get married?'

Ingrid shrugged, as if the matter were common knowledge. 'That's why I came here. Daddy said it was to learn about the shipping business—he owns a big shipping company in Copenhagen, and he and Greg are old friends, you see—but I knew he was hoping Greg and I would marry. And it was what I hoped, too, after I met Greg for the first time. He's so handsome, isn't he? I fell in love with him the moment I first saw him.'

Rose groaned inwardly. This was getting worse and worse. While Ingrid was obviously foolish and impulsive, her account of events seemed all too likely. Greg was certainly charismatic enough to turn any young girl's head, and Ingrid herself was so beautiful that it was hardly surprising if he had found her equally irresistible. What had his exact words been when he had described her earlier today? The kind of woman who could easily drive a man insane? At the time Rose had thought he was disparaging Ingrid, but now she was not so sure. Wasn't it exactly the kind of thing a man might say about the woman he loved? But surely Greg wouldn't lead a young, impressionable girl like Ingrid astray even if he did love her? Especially if he loved her! Wouldn't he insist that they had time apart so that she could be sure she knew her own mind before they made such a huge decision?

'I can't believe Greg invited you to stay in his house and then immediately seduced you!' Rose burst out.

Ingrid gave a watery giggle. 'Not immediately,' she agreed. 'We lived together for a long time—oh, months and months—before it happened. But all the time he could see I was in love with him and after a while he fell in love with me too and then...and then we started making love and everything was wonderful. Greg worshipped me.'

Rose felt a sudden spasm of doubt. Greg worshipping someone? It didn't sound likely. 'So what went wrong, if he thought you were so wonderful?' she asked rather curtly.

Ingrid's tears began to flow again in a blinding downpour. 'He got tired of me and made me leave. I suppose it was because he met you and had an affair with you.'

'Ingrid, don't you dare say that!' protested Rose. 'Greg and I are not having an affair.'

Ingrid looked up at her joyfully. 'You're not? Oh, promise me you're telling the truth.'

'Of course I'm telling the truth.'

'Then you won't go to bed with him, will you? If you're not already doing it, you won't start, will you? Oh, please, Rose, promise me you won't. If you'll just leave him alone, I know he'll come back to me sooner or later and marry me. I know he will.'

Rose gave the younger woman a troubled look. 'Ingrid, if what you're telling me is true, you'd be much better off without Greg. He can't possibly love you if he's treated you so callously.'

'He does!' retorted Ingrid defiantly, her blue eyes flashing. Then suddenly her expression changed. Instead of looking like an angry little girl, she looked like a weary, worldly wise shipping magnate. 'And anyway, even if he doesn't love me, that doesn't count in families like ours. It's very good business sense for Greg to marry me, my father said so. I'm an only child and all my family's assets will come into Greg's hands one day. That's very important to a man like him, who cares so much about success.'

'I don't think Greg cares about success,' protested Rose. 'If he ever does marry, it will be because he loves the woman he's marrying and for no other reason.'

'No, it won't!' said Ingrid stubbornly. 'I've known him longer than you. He only cares about building up his shipyard to make it the best in the world. He'll do anything for that.'

Rose opened her mouth to disagree and was struck by a sudden, unpleasant memory of Greg on the cliffs at Talland. What had he said to her that day? 'I think on the whole I'd prefer a straight-out marriage of convenience to all the drama women seem to thrive on. A marriage where you cemented business alliances by taking a bride with no wild expectations of living happily ever after.' She caught her breath in horror. Was Ingrid right? Could Greg really be so calculating, so hard-headed, so bent on pursuing his own financial advantage?

'He's not like that!' Rose insisted desperately. 'He wouldn't marry a woman he didn't love.'

'You're only saying that because you want him yourself!' Ingrid cried. 'But you're wasting your time. Even if he does go to bed with you, it won't make you happy. He'd only be having a last fling before he married me.'

Tears sparkled again in the younger woman's eyes and Rose, although more hurt and disturbed than she cared to admit, put out her hand in a protective gesture. Suddenly there was a footfall in the corridor and the sound of a deep masculine voice. Greg's voice.

'Ingrid? Rose?'

Ingrid clutched Rose's arm and spoke in an imploring stage whisper. 'Don't tell him what I said to you; he'd be furious if he knew I'd told you all our secrets.'

Greg's face was like thunder when he entered the tea-room and he showed very little sympathy for Ingrid's tears.

'I've told you before and I'll tell you again—I don't want to see any more of those prima donna performances!' he snapped. 'If you can't behave more sensibly,

I'll pack you off home to your father. Now go and wash your face.'

Ingrid's eyes were still brimming reproachfully as she trailed out of the room.

'Did you have to be so unkind?' demanded Rose as the sniffs diminished down the corridor.

'It only makes her worse when I'm nice to her,' growled Greg. 'And now I suppose she's filled your head with some cock-and-bull story in which I feature as Bluebeard?'

Rose's brows met in a perplexed frown. She had a shrewd suspicion that most of Ingrid's story was moonshine. And yet...

'It did sound a bit far-fetched,' she said slowly. 'But all the same... what did happen between you, Greg?'

'I don't intend to discuss it,' retorted Greg through his teeth. 'The whole affair was a ridiculous fiasco and the less that's known about it by outsiders, the better. The only thing I'll say is this. I don't believe I did anything to be ashamed of.'

'I see.' Rose kept her voice deliberately neutral, but she could not entirely suppress the uneasiness that stirred inside her. Would Greg consider an affair with a girl Ingrid's age something to be ashamed of or not? And was he really thinking of marrying her just to gain control of her assets?

'Do you? I wonder,' murmured Greg half to himself. Then he crossed the room and tilted Rose's chin so that his blazing brown eyes gazed intently down at her. 'Well, it really comes down to this, doesn't it? Do you trust me enough to continue our friendship? Or do you believe whatever Ingrid has told you?'

A tremor passed through Rose's body as much because of his nearness and the touch of his fingers as because of the question he was asking her. And yet the question was vitally important. Did she really believe that

Greg had been heartless enough to seduce and abandon a nineteen-year-old? Or to marry one purely for money? If that was true, then Rose certainly didn't want to be his next target for conquest. But was he really capable of being so selfish and unscrupulous? The evidence against it seemed quite damning and yet...

'No, I don't believe her!' Rose burst out. 'I won't believe it. I know you're scheming and deceitful and smooth-talking with more twists than a Cornish back alley, but I don't think you're downright rotten.'

'Thanks,' said Greg drily.

Rose gave an exasperated sigh. 'I'm defending you,' she pointed out.

'I know,' agreed Greg. 'Heaven help me if you ever decide to attack me!'

His dark eyes were glinting with amusement and for a moment Rose decided to return his gaze with dignity. Then her lips twitched and she gave a reluctant gasp of laughter.

'You're abominable, Greg!'

'Too abominable to have dinner with? I can promise you a really good meal, if you'll help me with my computer problems. I have a new computer-aided design program with a totally inadequate manual.'

They spent the remainder of the afternoon at the shipyard, where Rose became so absorbed in the CAD computer program that she forgot all about Ingrid's problems. Then afterwards they had pre-dinner drinks at Greg's home, followed by a stroll around the part of the city which had survived the bombing of World War Two. They visited the Barbican and the spot where the *Mayflower* had set sail and the statue of Sir Francis Drake on the Hoe. Although it was getting late, pale green twilight still illuminated the sky, making the city look like a stage backdrop with its yachts bobbing peacefully at anchor and its rows of terraced houses high on the ridge tops.

'I love the long summer evenings in Britain!' exclaimed Rose. 'There's nothing like this in the tropics back home. The sun just sinks into the sea like a cannonball at six o'clock, summer or winter.'

'There are magnificent sights there too,' pointed out Greg. 'The Great Barrier Reef, tropical rainforests, palm trees, gleaming white beaches...'

'Mm, that's all true,' admitted Rose. 'But somehow there's no real sense of tradition in Australia and I didn't know how much I missed that until I came here. I find England's old buildings and customs so fascinating that I don't think I'll ever want to leave.'

'You really think you'll settle here, then?'

It was such a loaded question that Rose stiffened and caught her breath. She must not read too much into this. It might be merely friendly curiosity on Greg's part, rather than any urgent personal wish to keep her here. And there were so many variables in her own life too. If Martin marries Delia, if I can manage to earn a living in England, if this friendship with Greg doesn't lead to disaster...

'Who knows?' she replied with a shrug, trying to keep her tone light.

'Well, seeing you're so keen on Merrie Olde Englande, I think I'll take you somewhere where they specialise in hearty British food,' said Greg equally lightly.

Rose exclaimed in delight over the low ceilings with their crooked oak beams, the panelled walls and crooked windows of the old tavern where Greg took her for dinner. After a long and pleasant agony of indecision, she decided on steak and kidney pudding, while Greg to her amazement ordered the Star-gazy pie, 'With fish heads, please.' When the food arrived, the waitress gazed questioningly at them.

'Star-gazy pie?' she asked.

'That's for the lady,' said Greg swiftly.

'But I ordered——' began Rose.

'Oh, no, my love, you must be mistaken,' insisted Greg with a glint in his eye. 'I'm sure the Star-gazy pie was yours. And you really wouldn't want to make a scene about it in a public restaurant, would you? I'll have the steak and kidney pudding, thanks.'

For a moment Rose contemplated rebellion, but the thought of foisting a plate of fish heads on an unwilling Greg was too horrific to bear. She sat fuming in silence, torn between rage and amusement, until the waitress had retreated.

'Is this your idea of revenge?' she hissed.

'Ooh, aah, you'm right there, m'dear,' replied Greg in a Cornish accent so thick that she could barely understand it. 'Eat hearty, now. It b'aint right to let a nice Star-gazy pie get cold.'

'You brute,' breathed Rose, suppressing a twinge of admiration at the way he had paid her back.

Yet Greg wasn't completely callous. He didn't touch the steak and kidney pudding and, after she had eaten the first fish head, he took pity on her and swapped plates. Rose began to enjoy herself and, as the evening wore on, she felt as if she were waltzing dizzily around a ballroom about six inches above the floor. Part of that effect might have been due to the glass of white wine she had with dinner or the hot, delicious punch at the jazz club afterwards, but most of it was due entirely to the intoxicating presence of Greg. He was the most extraordinary, baffling man she had ever met in her life, full of unexpected surprises. In some ways he was still a simple Cornish fisherman, in others an astute businessman with a sophistication that surprised her. Yet one thing she was sure of: wherever he went, Polperro or Plymouth or, for that matter, Panama or Puerto Rico, Greg would be totally in command of every situation. And he would always retain that vibrant, animal mag-

netism that both intrigued and frightened her. All the
same, in spite of the magnetic attraction she felt towards
Greg, Rose was still conscious of a barrier between them.
She might not believe everything Ingrid had told her,
but the Danish girl's outburst had set up a potent echo
inside her head. Try as she might to banish them, the
words kept whispering away... 'We fell in love and
started sleeping together ... sleeping together ... sleeping
together ...' Would she ever be able to trust Greg again?

It was after midnight when they returned to Pisky Bay
and when they stepped out of the car, by common
consent they stood in silence for a moment. The whole
place looked magical, with moonlight spilt in a milky
path across the dark, rippling seas. A light breeze was
stirring the elm trees, and a subdued scent of flowers
rose from the garden. As Greg led her to the front door
where the porch light shed a friendly pool of golden
radiance, Rose felt her muscles tense and her heart beat
faster with expectancy. Every nerve in her body yearned
for him and it was all she could do not to move into his
arms and raise her lips to his. Yet when Greg hauled her
into his arms and nuzzled her hair, her whole body stiffened. She didn't believe Ingrid, but she wasn't going to
take any chances...

'Don't, Greg,' she ordered, tearing free of his grip. 'I
told you, I only wanted to be friends with you.'

'Friends!' hissed Greg savagely, striking the column
of the porch with his clenched fist. 'All right, damn it!
I suppose that's better than nothing. But can I see you
next weekend?'

It was more than she could do to refuse. She stood
watching him from under half-closed eyelids, her pulses
racing and her breath coming unevenly. 'Yes,'
she gasped.

Then, turning away, she hurried inside.

* * *

It soon became the established pattern for Greg and Rose to spend their weekends together. With the help of a little advertising in the local tourist offices, the newly renovated cottage was doing a brisk trade in bed and breakfast, but this very prosperity brought some problems with it. Often the small house at Pisky Bay was so full of the clatter and conversation of paying guests and the ringing of telephones that Rose found it hard to concentrate on her computer programming. What was more, she found herself missing the privacy that she had been used to in Queensland. Although she was very fond of her mother, she had been living in her own flat for the last five years and found her habits of independence died hard. When she mentioned her problem casually to Greg, his solution was immediate.

'Come back and stay at my cottage during the week,' he suggested. 'There'll be no one here to disturb you, not even the telephone, and you can pop over easily enough in the daytime to help your mother when she's busy, especially if you buy a small car.'

Rose protested feebly, but eventually allowed herself to be persuaded. It was heaven to spend some quiet time alone at last and her computer programming progressed much faster. Before very long she completed the computer program she had been writing for Inglis's, sent it off to the company in Brisbane and was soon rewarded by a fat cheque and a letter of appreciation from Martin. The cheque pleased her. In spite of the current business at the cottage, she was well aware that bookings would soon drop off once the high summer period was over, and she was determined to keep up the payments on the bank loan without any help from Greg.

The letter from Martin affected her differently. At first she could not even bring herself to open it, and when she did she felt a mixture of relief and disappointment at its contents. It was simply a friendly, even flattering screed, extolling her virtues as an employee and saying how much Martin appreciated her work. There was no hint of any kind that their former love-affair had ever happened. Well, that was fine with Rose. If Martin was going to marry somebody else, there was obviously no point in his waxing lyrical over how much he had once loved her. But then why not stay completely businesslike? Why send her a long, handwritten letter full of company gossip and lots of private jokes as if they were still the best of friends? It didn't make sense and it annoyed Rose. Particularly since there were veiled references in it to the possibility of a new branch being opened in Britain shortly and more programming work to follow. All the same, whether for business reasons or for the kind of wishy-washy sentimentality that she despised, Rose kept the letter.

At the end of the first week of using Greg's cottage again, she held an anxious inner debate with herself about what she should do. Should she leave before he arrived, so as not to intrude on his privacy? But that seemed rather unfriendly, although she did not want to encroach on their newly patched-up friendship. In the end, she decided she would stay long enough to share a cup of coffee or a quick drink with Greg and then go home. But somehow Greg adroitly carried her off for a meal in a pub at Looe before she really knew what was going on, and that became the pattern of their weekends from that time onwards. Rose found the whole experience as nerve-racking as walking around the rim of a live volcano. Try as she might to keep a cool, restrained friendship going between the two of them, Greg had other ideas, and she often found herself dragged into a torrid embrace. To make matters worse, he had deliberately set out to charm her mother with gifts of flowers and chocolates so that Fay had defiantly declared her belief that Joan was wrong about him. In fact,

Rose's mother even seemed to do all she could to throw them together, taking on most of the bed-and-breakfast work herself.

This left Rose and Greg free to spend long, sunny, glorious days sailing, horse-riding and exploring the beaches and rock pools where Greg had played as a child. Sometimes they made excursions further afield with the car to St Michael's Mount and Lanhydrock and across the border into Devon to Buckland Abbey and Castle Drogo. They picnicked on Dartmoor, canoed on the River Tamar, went to open-air concerts and local markets and had a wonderful time. And each weekend Rose's uneasiness grew a little worse, because she knew that sooner or later it would all have to come to an end. It was madness to go on seeing Greg so frequently with nothing resolved between them, especially when she still found his physical magnetism as raw and compelling as ever. And that wasn't even the worst problem. The worst problem was that she was dangerously close to falling head over heels in love with him, which would be a crazy thing to do, especially as there was no sign that he felt anything more than a violent sexual attraction to her. And there was still the enigma of his relationship with Ingrid... No, the only sensible thing Rose could do was to leave Cornwall at the end of the summer and look for a job elsewhere.

Then one day at the end of summer they had a conversation that brought matters to a head. All through July and August the weather had been glorious, hot, sunny and perfect. But now for the first time there was a sudden change. One Saturday afternoon grey clouds blew in from the east and rain began to explode against the glass windows of the conservatory like a hail of bullets. Greg, who had been lounging back in one of the leather couches, tossed aside his newspaper and rose to his feet with a pleased smile on his face.

'Well, time to light a fire, I think,' he announced. 'We can move into the sitting-room and get cosy.'

Half an hour later they were sitting in front of the roaring blaze while the rain drummed noisily on the roof and the sea was hidden in a grey haze. Rose gazed pensively into the heart of the crackling orange flames, trying to work up the resolve to tell Greg of her decision. That she must leave Cornwall soon and see a lot less of him in future. The trouble was that she didn't trust herself to explain why without getting upset. While she was still brooding over the matter, Greg suddenly took her by surprise with an unexpected question.

'What do you like to do in winter?' he demanded.

Rose looked mildly perplexed. 'I've never really had a winter,' she replied. 'You don't if you live in the tropics.'

'Have you ever seen snow?' asked Greg.

'No.' Rose's eyes were suddenly wide and shining, like a child's. 'Actually, it might be rather fun, especially at Christmas.'

'It will be fun,' insisted Greg, as if he were daring it to be anything else. 'I'll tell you what we'll do: I'll buy the biggest Christmas tree you've ever seen and we'll have roast turkey and plum pudding and carols, and if it doesn't have the decency to snow in Cornwall I'll take you to Scotland for Christmas. We'll have a wonderful time, my love.'

We. Rose's heart began to hammer furiously at that simple little word. Half of her felt touched and excited beyond measure that Greg was already making plans months ahead, plans which included her. Yet the other part was deeply suspicious, with a wariness born of disillusion. Greg hadn't given her the slightest clue about the terms on which he saw her travelling to Scotland with him and it wasn't going to be altogether easy trying to find out. Oh, she could ask, but would he tell her the truth? And what could she say without feeling utterly ridiculous? Excuse me, Greg, but could you just clarify that suggestion for me? Were you thinking of a quick proposal of marriage before we left? Or do you want me to go as your mistress? Or—oh, that wonderful stand-by of scheming males!—are we going to be 'just good friends'? Trip to Scotland, indeed! No, snow didn't seem quite wonderful enough to justify the risk. Much better to keep a safe distance from Greg's little plans...

'That's very kind of you,' said Rose calmly. 'But I don't know if I'll even be here at Christmas time.'

'Why not?' demanded Greg with a frown.

'I might go to London and look for a job now that my mother is properly settled in.'

'Why would you do a crazy thing like that?'

'It's not crazy!' retorted Rose, stung by his tone. 'We're not very well off, you know. The bed-and-breakfast trade is fine at the moment but it's bound to drop off once the summer is over. In the meantime we've both got to live and I've got a bank loan to repay. I can only do that if I get a job. That freelance work I was doing for Martin's company is finished now too, so I've got to find a new source of income.'

Greg's face darkened at the mention of Martin's name and he gave an exasperated snort. 'Look, if it's only a question of money, my love,' he said impatiently, 'you've nothing to worry about. I'm guarantor for your house loan and that's nothing but a drop in the ocean to me. And if you and Fay need money to live on, you've only to say the word and——'

'No!' shouted Rose. 'I've got my pride.'

'I know you have. Too damned much pride,' growled Greg. 'Why won't you let me help you?'

'Because...because...I'm nothing to you. We're just...friends...and...oh, leave it, Greg. Let's just say I want to live in London.'

Greg dismissed that idea. 'You wouldn't like London,' he said rudely.

The assertion infuriated Rose. 'How do you know?'

'Because you're so starry-eyed about village life. Anyway, I know you fairly well by now.'

'Do you just? You're very sure of yourself after only a couple of months, part of which time we weren't even speaking to each other.'

'It doesn't matter. First impressions are what count. Anyway, I'm a good judge of character.'

'Really?' purred Rose. 'So what judgements have you reached about my character?'

'That you're old-fashioned and simple,' said Greg triumphantly. 'And much better suited to staying in Cornwall than in London.'

Old-fashioned, simple? Next he'd be expecting her to knit him socks or hand-churn butter! Rose gave him a burning look. 'Thanks for the character reading,' she said sceptically. 'Do you do palmistry too, by any chance?'

'I could,' agreed Greg with a provocative glint in his eyes. 'And if I did, I'd tell you that your future lay with a tall, dark stranger and a sea voyage.'

'Meaning you on a sailing boat from Polperro to Fowey?'

'Why not? You'd certainly enjoy it more than moving to London. You and I have something special going, Rose, and you know it. So stop talking rubbish, my dear, and tell me how much you want.'

He had actually reached into the inner pocket of his jacket which was lying over a chair and pulled out a cheque-book before Rose could find words to reply. The arrogance of it, the sheer, breathtaking confidence that the whole disagreement was about money and could be settled with the stroke of a pen, almost choked her. Couldn't he see that what she wanted from him wasn't a financial settlement but a settlement of the gnawing emotional doubts that were driving them apart? A simple, honest statement about what his feelings and intentions towards her were? And a reassurance that he wasn't involved with Ingrid?

'I don't want anything from you!' she shouted. 'And as for your fortune-telling skills, how do you know my future doesn't contain a tall, fair stranger and an air trip to Australia?'

'What's that supposed to mean?' Greg's voice was suddenly hushed and oddly dangerous.

Rose was already beginning to regret her impulsive words, but some madness drove her on. 'I still have an open return ticket to Australia and I might decide to use it if I don't like England. Martin's not married yet, only engaged. And he's been writing to me. He might change his mind and marry me.'

'In a pig's eye, he will!' sneered Greg. 'Don't kid yourself, Rose. He'll never marry you in a million years. You're too ordinary.'

'Thanks very much!'

She was so angry and hurt by his taunt that she had to bite the back of her hand to hold back the tears. Suddenly Greg swore under his breath and grabbed her arm.

'You are the most exasperating woman,' he growled. 'Are you crying?'

'No. I'm just taking deep, cleansing breaths while I reflect on your simple wisdom, Greg. It's so refreshing of you to remind me that I'm too ordinary and boring for anybody ever to want to marry me.'

Greg swore again, more violently. 'Don't be a fool, I didn't say that.'

'A fool too, thank you. Ordinary, boring and a fool.'

'Rose,' shouted Greg, transferring his grip to her shoulders and shaking her. 'Shut up! I didn't say that you were too ordinary for anybody to want to marry you, I said *he* wouldn't.' His voice was full of loathing as he spoke the word 'he'.

'Why wouldn't he?' cried Rose.

'Because if he didn't see the value of what he had while you were in his arms . . . and his bed, why the hell would he see it now? You're a wonderful person, Rose, warm and loving and tantalising with a unique sense of humour, but I doubt if that swine Inglis ever appreciated you or is ever likely to.'

This grudging rush of compliments delivered in a rapid, angry burst had a surprising effect on Rose. She took a swift, unsteady breath and looked up at Greg with wide eyes and quivering lips. He gave a low groan, and for an instant something fierce and stormy and possessive blazed in his eyes. In that moment she could easily have melted into his arms and yielded totally to him. Astonishingly, since he had always seemed only too anxious for such a union, Greg suddenly snatched his hands away from her shoulders as urgently as if he'd been stung.

'I'm not going to fall into the same trap twice,' he muttered under his breath. 'Get your things, Rose, and I'll drive you home.'

Rose's heart was still thudding tumultuously when they reached the cottage at Pisky Bay and a swift glimpse of Greg's granite profile did not reassure her. What did he mean about 'falling into the same trap twice' and where did they go from here? With the violent animosity seething between them at the moment, it hardly seemed likely that it would be 'business as usual' next weekend. She was still biting her lip and stealing unhappy glances at Greg, when a figure came hurrying down the drive in the soaking rain. It was Fay with a huge black umbrella over her head. Rose opened the car door, letting in a rush of chill air and the smell of sodden earth and plants.

'Oh, there you are, my love,' cried her mother in a worried voice. 'Hurry up and come inside. There's a long-distance phone call for you from Australia. Rose...it's Martin!'

CHAPTER EIGHT

Rose's heart was beating unevenly with apprehension as she picked up the telephone receiver. 'Hello?' she said warily.

Martin's voice came booming down the line. Usually it had a fruity, confiding tone, but the telephone gave it a rather hollow ring.

'Rose? Wonderful to hear your voice, sweetie. Martin here. Did you get my letter?'

'Yes,' said Rose.

'I just wanted to tell you that I'm very pleased with your work. That stock-control program that you wrote for us is already saving us a mint, but I've also got a business proposal that I want to discuss with you. Now listen; I'm opening a UK branch of Inglis's in the new year and I'll be flying over to London this week to do some preliminary investigation of warehouse sites and so on. I'm going to need a good systems manager to work for me and I thought the job might possibly suit you. Would you like to have lunch and talk about it?'

Rose gave a soft gasp as a feeling of complete turmoil swept over her. She was annoyed at Martin's cool presumption that they could pick up their business relationship with no reference whatsoever to their shattered personal one. All the same, she felt professionally flattered by his approval of her work, and the prospect of earning some money was certainly tempting. But antagonism and wounded pride were certainly uppermost when she replied.

'Lunch?' she said noncommittally. 'I don't know about that, Martin. Where do you want me to meet you?'

'In London, of course,' he said with a touch of impatience. 'You can leave your eggs and bacon and your bed-making for a day or two and catch a train up, can't you?'

His patronising reference to her bed-and-breakfast business hit a raw nerve and Rose felt a sudden flash of annoyance. Why should she go traipsing halfway across England just to please Martin, when he had treated her so badly?

'It's not quite that simple, Martin,' she said curtly. 'Actually I'm rather busy at the moment.'

'All right, then,' growled Martin. 'I'll come down and visit you in Cornwall. I suppose I ought to take a look at the place anyway while I'm in England. Does Friday suit you?'

Rose glanced around for a pen and pad and became suddenly aware of Greg lounging against the hall wall with his arms folded. From the intent expression in his eyes, she felt sure that he was shamelessly trying to eavesdrop and the resentful scowl on his face left her in no doubt that he was jealous. The thought gave her enormous pleasure. After all the heartache he had put her through over Ingrid, it would serve him right to suffer a few pangs of uncertainty himself.

'That would be fine, Martin,' she said with more warmth in her voice. 'Let's say lunch this Friday in Looe. That's the closest town to where I live. You can get a train from Paddington in the morning and I'll meet you at Looe station at about twelve-thirty.'

'Great,' agreed Martin. 'I can't wait to see you again, gorgeous.'

Rose smiled sceptically at that. 'Tell me, Martin, how are the wedding plans coming along?' she shot back.

There was a gloomy sigh at the other end of the line. 'They're not,' growled Martin. 'It's all been postponed.'

'Postponed?' echoed Rose in shock. 'But why?'

'I'll tell you about it on Friday. Look, I'd better go now. Goodbye.'

'Goodbye,' murmured Rose, putting down the phone. Greg and Fay both gazed at her expectantly.

'What was that all about?' demanded her mother.

Swiftly Rose explained the gist of her conversation with Martin.

'You're not seriously thinking of going to work for him in London, are you?' snapped Greg.

Rose tossed her head defiantly. 'Why not?' she asked in a hard voice. 'There's no real future for me in Cornwall, is there?'

For a moment Greg looked as if he was about to speak, then he flashed a swift glance at Rose's mother, gritted his teeth and remained silent. It was left to Fay to twitter around and make objections.

'Rose, are you sure you want to have lunch with him? I know he paid you very well for the computer programming, but he treated you so badly in Australia. I don't like to think——'

'Mum, it's my business and there are important matters I need to discuss with Martin. Now can we please drop the subject?'

It was another dismal, rainy day when Martin arrived in Looe to have lunch with her. A grey mist lay in long, trailing scarves along the green hilltops, a fine rain was drizzling down and the sea was as dark as beaten pewter. Rose's spirits were as dismal as the weather. It had been nearly three months now since she had last seen Martin and, to be painfully honest, she hadn't really thought about him much in that time, but now his imminent arrival had woken all the old turmoil inside her. How would she feel when she saw him? Would she still want to run and put her arms around him and claim him as her own, even though he was engaged to another woman? Would she still feel the same pain and betrayal and anguish that she had felt when he had first told her about Delia? Or had the anger and hurt pride died down? The uncertainty, the fear of making a fool of herself, the mingled hope and elation and resentment made her pace restlessly backwards and forwards on the wet platform, until the elderly train finally made its unhurried arrival into the station. And then she saw him. Tall, blond and imperious, muffled in a thick camel-hair coat, he stepped off the train and sniffed the damp, salt air with a discontented expression.

'Martin!' cried Rose and hurried across to meet him.

He looked a shade plumper than she remembered and she noticed for the first time that his blond hair was beginning to recede around the temples and that there were tiny, broken red veins scattered across his nose and cheeks. When Rose had first met him five years ago he had had the bronzed, muscular physique of an athlete and sportsman. Now too much high living had begun to blur his clean-cut appearance. With a slight feeling of shock she realised that although he was only twenty-eight years old he was beginning to look a good eight or ten years older. But there was no mistaking the gleam in his green eyes as he flung his arms around her and kissed her warmly on the mouth.

'Rose! Great to see you, sweetheart! But I thought this was supposed to be summertime. Feels more like winter to me.'

'It's been lovely up until now,' retorted Rose with spirit. 'And it's still very pretty, even when it does rain.'

'Humph,' scoffed Martin. 'Well, give me a nice Gold Coast beach any day of the week. All right, now where can we get a taxi to take us to this restaurant?'

'I thought we'd walk,' said Rose. 'It's only a few hundred yards and most of the streets are closed to traffic. I've brought an umbrella, so we won't get too wet.'

Martin rolled his eyes, but allowed her to put up the umbrella over his head. They walked along beside the river in silence, except for the hiss of car tyres on the wet road and the occasional, mournful cry of a seagull. When they reached the bridge and plunged into the maze of tiny streets and quaint old houses that led down to the seashore, Rose waited expectantly for Martin to exclaim over the picturesque beauty of the old town of East Looe. Instead he simply shook his head disparagingly.

'It could do with a bit of modernising, couldn't it?' he demanded.

'Martin!' cried Rose indignantly. 'It's the old, traditional atmosphere that gives it its charm!'

Martin grinned. 'Oh, well, you always were a sucker for tradition, weren't you, Rosie? So are we going to eat in some medieval hovel where I'll hit my head on the ceiling when I stand up?'

'Yes,' snapped Rose. 'But it's not a hovel. It's a wonderful little tavern with lots of atmosphere.'

But even the oak beams, mullioned windows, cosy wooden booths and crackling log fire failed to impress Martin. Watching him gaze around the tavern with a martyred expression, Rose could guess perfectly well that he would much rather have been in some showy new restaurant full of glass and chrome. Had their tastes always been so different? Or had she simply changed since moving to Cornwall? Suddenly she felt a desperate need to understand what was going on.

'So what happened between you and Delia?' she asked as they came to the end of their meal of delicious roast beef, crusty Yorkshire pudding and baked vegetables.

Martin dabbed his mouth with a napkin and leaned back in his chair before picking up his beer mug again. He was getting a bit of a paunch, Rose noticed.

'It was your doing, really,' he said thoughtfully, after taking a long gulp of beer.

'My doing?' echoed Rose incredulously. 'What do you mean? How could it be my doing?'

Martin gave a gusty sigh. 'Well, you know what women are like,' he complained. 'Somebody spilt the beans to Delia about how I'd been involved with you and she hit the roof. Called me a two-timing bastard and said she wasn't going to marry me.'

'Good for her,' said Rose coldly.

Martin stared at her, aghast. 'Oh, come on, Rosie,' he pleaded in an injured voice. 'It was just a bit of fun between you and me. We never meant anything serious by it. She should have understood that.'

Rose almost leapt to her feet in indignation and then her rage was swept away by a half-hysterical urge to burst out laughing. What did it matter anyway? Had she ever really believed herself in love with this self-satisfied fool who was sitting here expecting her to be patient and understanding? All those occasions when she had soothed Martin's wounded pride over some ridiculous incident at work suddenly rose before her and she felt a shaky sense of relief that she no longer had to bother with him, no longer had to pretend. Had he always had this childish belief that the universe revolved around him? Had he always been so selfish and uncaring of other people's feelings? Yes, he had! They why had it taken her so long to see it? Well, now that she had, he would no longer have the power to hurt her ever again. And that was a relief, an incredible relief. She felt like a child who had been badly frightened by a Hallowe'en mask and was now old enough to realise that it was nothing but a harmless illusion.

'Poor Martin,' she said with a touch of mockery.

'I knew you'd understand, Rosie,' he said. 'You always were a good sort. The trouble with Delia is she's been spoilt rotten and she just doesn't realise she's got to make an effort to please a man. She thinks she can just walk in and change my whole life. Well, I don't suppose this tiff's anything serious and I certainly don't want the marriage plans to fall through. Her old man's one of the biggest resort developers in Queensland. All the same, she's going to have to pull her socks up if she wants to get me back...'

Rose sat back and closed her eyes for a moment, letting Martin ramble on while her own thoughts were far away. She found his grumbling so absurd that it was almost soothing. How different he was from Greg! Greg was even wealthier and more successful, but he had never let wealth distort his view of the world the way Martin had done. Whatever his faults, nobody could accuse Greg of being pompous and self-satisfied. Infuriating, yes. Secretive, certainly. But not blinded by money. The first time she had met him she had believed he was a fisherman, and that wasn't only because of his clothing. It was because he still had the raw vitality and power of a man who had to wrestle his living from the hostile forces of nature. You could put Greg down in a jungle with nothing but his bare hands and he would survive. When it came down to it, he was still a savage at heart. Lean, hungry, untamed and full of primitive passion and vitality—just the way Rose wanted him to be. And with a rising sense of excitement she realised something else: Greg was her man and she was going to fight for him if necessary, even against that glamorous Danish girl. Martin's words came to her, far off and blurred as if they were being broadcast through fog.

'...new premises...outskirts of London...huge
European market. Now, to start with you'll be in charge
of a staff of about twelve, but later——'

'No,' said Rose clearly, emerging from her trance.

'Eh? What do you mean, "no"?' Martin's flushed
face made him look as aggressive as a turkey.

'I won't be in charge of a staff of twelve, because I'm
not taking the job,' replied Rose apologetically.

'What? You've brought me all the way down here and
you've got the hide to tell me you're not taking the job?
Why not? Aren't I offering you enough money?'

'It's not that.'

'I know what it is! You're jealous of Delia.'

Rose contemplated explaining and then sighed and
shook her head. Martin would never in a million years
understand why she preferred Greg to him, unless she
told him that Greg was richer. And it had nothing to do
with that. It was because Greg made her laugh and cry
and rage and feel alive in every cell of her body...

'No, I'm not jealous of Delia,' she said with a wry
smile. 'Actually, I'm rather sorry for her.'

'Sorry?' demanded Martin belligerently. 'She's going
to marry one of the most successful men in Australia
and you're sorry for her? What the hell do you mean
by that?'

'Oh, never mind,' said Rose. 'You wouldn't understand anyway. You and I are light-years away from each
other, Martin, and I never realised it until now.'

Martin looked indignant and baffled. Then his face
lit up. 'You can deny it all you like,' he said with the air
of a detective solving the final clue to a mystery. 'But I
know it's Delia that's upset you, Rose. And I don't blame
you for that. As a matter of fact, I'm still fond of you
too. Bloody fond of you.' His hand closed over hers.
'What do you say we get back together and give it
another go?'

Rose stared at him incredulously. 'Martin, are you asking me to marry you?' she demanded.

'Marry?' A stricken look crossed his face and his large red hand retreated hastily across the tablecloth to the safety of his beer mug. 'Look, love, marriage wasn't quite what I had in mind——'

Rose dropped her eyes and choked back a hysterical urge to giggle. 'Nothing else will do for me, Martin,' she said sadly. 'So I'm afraid it's all over between us.'

For a disappointed lover, Martin made a remarkably swift recovery.

'Hell, Rose, I'm sorry,' he muttered. Then his face brightened. 'But I can see your point. Look, what about the job, then? Won't you give it another go? You're a damn good programmer and I'd hate to lose you.'

'Thanks, Martin,' said Rose with a touch of irony. 'It's nice to know how much you value me, but I don't want the job, either.'

'But there's all that work you've done on the inventory system! The program you sent us was great, but from what you said you've got heaps more data on sales projections too. Can't I even get access to that?'

'You're welcome to it,' said Rose coolly. 'Come back with me now and I'll copy it all on to disk for you. Then you needn't feel that you've had a wasted trip down here and we can say goodbye with no hard feelings.'

'All right, that's very decent of you,' agreed Martin with obvious relief.

They called for the bill, which Martin paid and then walked back to the car park by the bridge where Rose had left her car. All her computer equipment was at Greg's cottage, so she drove straight there.

'Nice view you have here,' commented Martin as they pulled up in the driveway. 'Er—your mother's not home today, is she? She never did take to me much, somehow.'

With a twinge of amusement, Rose realised that Martin thought this was her own cottage, but it hardly seemed worthwhile explaining the truth. 'No, she's away on a shopping trip in Plymouth,' she said. 'Now come inside and I'll get the disks for you.'

Twenty minutes later, Rose shut down the computer and handed a box of floppy disks to Martin. 'There you are,' she said. 'I hope you'll find them useful.'

As Martin set the disks down on the table, she realised with a twinge of alarm that he was looking not at the box but at her. A sudden gleam came into his eye and he caught his breath. Then he made a lunge at her and hugged her so hard that her ribs almost cracked.

'Come on, Rosie,' he urged. 'Change your mind and come to London with me. We'll stay at the Ritz and I'll take you to bed in the most luxurious suite they've got. Afterwards we'll paint the town red. You'll enjoy it.'

There was a cold rush of air at the living-room door and an even colder voice rang out through the room. Greg's voice.

'Like hell she will.'

He advanced a couple of paces into the room and stood with his feet planted wide apart and his hands resting on his hips. Every line in his body radiated aggression. His black eyebrows were drawn together, his eyes were narrowed and glittering, his mouth was set in a hard line and his whipcord muscles were tensed for action. He was dressed in faded jeans, scuffed fisherman's boots and a coarse woollen jersey with the sleeves rolled up to reveal his powerful tanned forearms. And the expression on his face was frankly murderous.

'Who the hell is this bloke, Rose?' demanded Martin, stepping back a pace.

'I... He... the cottage,' she stammered disjointedly. It was hard to believe that she had once won an award for public speaking.

Greg came to her rescue. 'I own this house and I live here with Rose,' he announced with a fine disregard for truth. 'So let me tell you, she doesn't want your job, or your slimy invitation to the Ritz.'

Martin turned to her with a stunned expression. 'Is this true?'

Rose opened her mouth twice and closed it again. Trying to explain Greg's elastic idea of the truth was too much for her. All the same, what he was telling Martin about her intentions was basically correct. 'Yes,' she said weakly.

'Well, you don't have to stay with him!' snorted Martin. His face turned a shade redder and his eyes travelled disdainfully round the room with its antique furniture and faded rugs. 'He can't be much of a man if this clapped-out old dump is the best he can offer you. I'll give you a luxury apartment in Mayfair, Rose.'

Greg advanced threateningly on the burly Australian. 'You'll get out of here, or I'll knock your head off,' he said in a voice soft with menace.

Martin squared his shoulders and punched one fist into the other as he scrutinised Greg from under lowered brows. Then, after a moment, he smiled uneasily, wiped the palms of his hands on his thighs and retreated prudently across the room. 'I don't want to upset Rose, or I'd take you up on that, you Cornish ratbag,' he blustered. 'But in any case, I don't approve of violence. Rose, can you give me a lift back to town?'

'No, she can't,' said Greg grimly.

Martin looked momentarily disconcerted. 'Well, can you call me a taxi, then?'

'There's no phone,' murmured Rose.

'No phone?' echoed Martin as if he had just been told the house had no roof.

'You can walk across the cliff path to Polperro and phone a taxi from there,' rapped out Greg.

'But it's bloody raining!' objected Martin in an outraged voice.

Greg strode into the hall and returned with an old umbrella which had survived from his early fishing days. 'Take this,' he ordered. 'Catch.'

Sulkily Martin fielded the object and opened it out, revealing two broken ribs that made it hang like an injured bat. 'I don't believe this,' he groaned. 'Rose, what about my box of disks?'

'I'm sure Greg won't mind if you take them,' said Rose mildly.

Martin edged past Greg as if he were a sleeping lion, grabbed the box of disks and headed for the door. But as he reached it he turned and looked back at Rose. 'Are you sure this is really what you want?' he asked.

Rose cast a swift sideways glance at Greg, who put his arm around her and dragged her possessively against him. This blatant show of masculine strength infuriated her, but at the same time she could not suppress a primitive thrill of pride and excitement at his ruthlessness. Her voice was halfway between laughter and rage as she replied. 'Yes, Martin, I'm sure.'

Martin rolled his eyes heavenwards. 'Women!' he muttered. 'I'd rather face a trade union picket line any day.'

Releasing his hold on Rose, Greg escorted the Australian out of the room in murderous silence. Rose darted into the hall just in time to see Greg slamming the conservatory door after the other man and actually locking it for once. He came stalking back with the restless, menacing tread of an angry panther. His dark eyes were narrowed and his usually lazy smile was replaced by a fierce scowl.

'Poor Martin,' murmured Rose. 'Did you have to behave like such a brute?'

'Yes,' said Greg through his teeth. 'It's useless to expect a man to be civilised when he's in love.'

Rose felt as shocked as if the ground had just moved under her feet.

'W-what did you say?' she breathed.

'You heard me! I love you, Rose. For heaven's sake, you must know that by now.'

'Must I?' she demanded unsteadily. 'When you've never said a word to suggest that you really cared about me, when you won't even tell me what's going on between you and Ingrid?'

Greg swore under his breath. 'Nothing is going on between me and Ingrid. There never has been, there never will be and if I'd had my way you and I would have been lovers weeks ago. I would have had you in my arms, in my bed, possessing you utterly. But you insisted that you only wanted friendship from me and I was afraid of ruining things between us if I said too much. I went too fast for you once already, Rose. This time I couldn't risk frightening you away. I had to wait and give you time before I could tell you how much I needed you. Sometimes I could hardly sleep at night for wanting you. I used to lie awake and burn for you.'

Rose's legs felt suddenly too weak to hold her. Shock and joy and relief flooded through her and for an instant she had to clutch the back of a chair to steady herself. It was true, then. He did love her, and that meant that Ingrid's intricately woven stories were nothing but wild invention . . . She could scarcely take it in.

'Do you mean this?' she asked hoarsely.

'Of course I mean it,' snarled Greg. 'And then, when I was being so patient, to find that smarmy bastard was coming down here to worm his way back into your good books just made me see red! I couldn't work all week for thinking how much I'd like to choke him and then to come home today and find him touching you and asking you to go off with him…he's lucky I didn't break his neck! When I think what might have happened if I hadn't arrived when I did——'

'Why did you arrive just then?' interrupted Rose. 'You don't usually come home till Friday evening.'

Greg scowled at her. 'Do you really think I could stay at work, knowing you were meeting him? I've been home since this morning but I couldn't settle to anything, especially once lunchtime came and I knew you were with him, so I went down and helped Charlie Polglaze sand his boat. It's amazing how much aggression you can take out on a battered old hull. I was coming back to get cleaned up and visit you when I walked in on you and lover boy.' The contempt in his voice was so scathing that Rose had to bite back a smile.

'You've got a piece of wood-shaving in your hair,' she murmured, reaching up to remove the feathery pink curl of wood.

'Don't tempt me, woman,' growled Greg, trapping her in an iron embrace and drawing her against him. 'It's not wise to put your arms around a man's neck unless you want something like this to happen.'

'This' was a long, bruising kiss that sent molten fire pulsing through her veins. She swallowed twice and then lifted trembling, parted lips for more.

'Oh, Greg,' she breathed, clinging to him weakly.

His face was buried in her hair, his voice muffled by its fragrant thickness. 'Rose, you weren't really planning to go off with that oaf, were you?'

'Of course not, Greg. How could I, when I'm in love with you?'

She heard his sharp intake of breath, then he hauled her against him, driving his pelvis into hers so that she felt the crude, raw power of his male arousal.

'Say that again Rose,' he rasped. 'Say it again. And again. And again.' The words came out in a harsh,

staccato rhythm and at each repetition his body thrust
violently against hers. Dizzying waves of arousal
throbbed through her and she let herself sway against
him, standing on tiptoe to plant small, nuzzling kisses
along his jawline and the sensitive skin near his ear.

'I'm in love with you, Greg,' she repeated.

'You little witch,' hissed Greg. 'I'm going to have you
and have you and have you until you beg for mercy.'

His urgent, demanding hands caught at her breasts,
but his touch was so skilful that she gave a low moan
of pleasure as he unbuttoned her blouse and continued
his exploration of her body. As deftly as if he already
knew every intimate detail of her response, he began to
rub his fingers around her nipples in tingling, featherlight circles until the sensitive peaks hardened and a
shudder went through her entire body.

'Well,' he murmured, his warm breath tickling her ear.
'What have you got to say to that, my love?'

'Yes,' she gasped, arching her back and thrusting
herself against his caressing hands. 'Yes, yes, yes, please,
Greg.'

With a muffled groan he released his hold on her
breasts, flung an arm around her waist and marched her
up the stairs as urgently as if they were abandoning a
sinking ship. When they reached the landing, he paused
for another long, devouring kiss, then wrenched open
the door of Rose's room.

'Oh, God, I want you,' he muttered.

The rain was still drumming a steady tattoo on the
roof and Rose could hear the distant roar of the sea
crashing on the rocks far below, but the room was warm
from the radiator under the window. She hesitated for
an instant, paralysed by a sudden sense of shyness as
her eyes darted over the huge, carved mahogany bed
covered with an old-fashioned cream and burgundy quilt.

'Don't be afraid, my love,' murmured Greg, bending to whisper in her ear. 'We've got all the time in the world. Time for you to catch fire and want me as badly as I want you.' He kissed her softly, letting his warm, moist tongue probe the inner surface of her ear so that she quivered under his touch.

'I already do,' she breathed. And, reaching for him, she thrust her hands up under the prickly wool of his jumper and felt the warm, hard, muscular planes of his torso.

'Oh, yes, yes,' he urged, seizing her hand and guiding it down below the waistband of his jeans. 'Touch me, Rose, fondle me. Let me go off my head with excitement.'

As feverishly as if they were the last man and woman on earth, they began hauling off each other's clothes, pausing to kiss and gasp and mutter disjointed endearments. But before long Greg had flung back the covers and they were lying in the middle of the vast bed together. Rose gasped at the touch of the cotton sheets on her skin.

'Oh, it's cold,' she protested.

'I'll soon warm you up,' promised Greg, drawing the feather duvet over their heads like a tent and seizing her. She closed her eyes and gave a long sigh of contentment at the pressure of his powerful, warm, muscular body crushing her so satisfactorily beneath him. An aching, primitive thrill of contentment filled her at the way they complemented each other. He was hard and masculine and demanding where she was soft and feminine and yielding, but it was exactly as it should be. She wanted it no other way. When his powerful hands began to move over her body, seizing and stroking her flesh, she sighed and arched herself against him.

'Getting warmer?' he asked in his deep Cornish burr.

'Yes,' she admitted, 'but I can't see you.'

He flung back the quilt, revealing his head and shoulders, and laughed down at her, his dark eyes glittering and his face alight with smouldering desire. 'Time enough for you to see me later,' he growled softly. 'Just for now I think it would be better if you feel me. Close your eyes, Rose, and lie back and let me explore you.'

With a faint giggle of protest, she obeyed. The light flared orange through her closed eyelids and all her other senses seemed to waken into heightened consciousness. She heard the window behind her head rattle in a sudden gust of wind, felt a brief rush of cool air then Greg's mouth came down on hers again. He smelled of salt water and wood-shavings, along with the spicy tang of his deodorant and some indefinable essence that was blantantly and unmistakably male. His chin had already began to develop five-o'clock shadow and as the rough skin scraped against her cheek she felt every nerve in her body quiver in response. But it was his kisses that roused her most. His mouth was warm, enticing, provocative. His tongue slid between her lips, and as it did so his fingers began to move further down on her body, tantalising her with a sly, suggestive touch that made her gasp and shudder. Drawing himself up on his forearms, Greg let his thick, glossy hair brush against her face and then turned to kiss the rest of her body.

By the time he had come to an end, every inch of her from her shoulders to the tips of her toes was quivering and pulsating with an aching, physical need so intense that she could never have dreamed it was possible. Greg too was aflame with desire, his body hot and hard and his eyes so dark and strange that she hardly recognised him. At last, when she felt she could bear it no longer, he poised himself above her and spoke in a low, harsh voice. 'Are you ready, my love?'

'Oh, yes, yes,' she gasped.

What followed was a revelation for Rose. She and Martin had shared a bed and yet she realised now that her deepest capacity for love and arousal had remained unawakened. Never, never in her life had she imagined that there could be such a blissful sense of union, such an annihilating, pulse-racing ecstasy as this. Their breathing came in fast, shallow gulps, they strained against each other as if they could obliterate all barriers. Their souls were fused as recklessly as their mouths and limbs. An alarming crescendo of need and love and indescribable yearning began to build and build deep inside Rose until finally it reached an explosive climax. Every muscle in her body tensed and a low, unearthly cry escaped her lips. Greg gripped her hard against him, enveloping her in his arms and a moment later he too cried out, before collapsing spent and shuddering against her. They lay together for a long time, hot and sweaty and breathing fast as if they had run some extraordinary race, but filled with a happiness too deep for words.

'I love you,' he said at last, bending forward to kiss her on her eyelids and nose and lips. 'I love you, I love you, I love you.'

She smiled and nuzzled her face against his. 'I love you, too,' she said contentedly. 'Oh, Greg, this is the happiest moment of my life.'

It was nearly suppertime when Rose arrived home and the sound of a cheerful soprano voice belting out Gilbert and Sullivan lyrics made it obvious where her mother was. She pushed open the kitchen door and grinned as Fay stopped on a high C. The table was set with a red-checked tablecloth, a terracotta pot of red geraniums, blue and white china and gleaming silver. In the background, saucepans were bubbling merrily on top of the Aga stove and the air was filled with the aromas of chicken soup and apple pie. It all looked cosy and welcoming, but Rose didn't have long to admire it. Fay took one look at her radiant face and gasped.

'Greg's popped the question, hasn't he?' she demanded eagerly.

Rose stepped back a pace and a bright scarlet blush flooded through her entire face and neck. 'No,' she cried in outrage.

'Well, something marvellous has happened to you, hasn't it?'

Rose hung her head. 'Well, Greg did tell me he loved me,' she admitted.

Fay collapsed in the chair with an ecstatic sigh and poured herself a glass of scrumpy. 'It won't be long, then,' she announced. 'He's not the kind of man to beat about the bush. I think a June wedding would be lovely, myself. I said as much to Joan Penwithick only this afternoon.'

Rose was speechless for a moment.

'Mum, you're impossible,' she wailed at last. 'I suppose you and Joan even planned the bridesmaids' dresses!'

Fay smiled guiltily. 'Well, I did think coral-pink chiffon would be nice,' she said. 'And perhaps satin for you with tiny seed-pearls on the bodice.'

Rose groaned and rolled her eyes. 'I give up,' she cried. 'You embarrass me to death. Well, don't you dare say a word of this to Greg!'

'No, dear, I wouldn't dream of it. Not until everything's settled, anyway.'

Rose shook her head despairingly and stole a couple of carrot sticks from the chopping board. 'I won't let you near him next weekend,' she threatened. 'I don't trust you.'

'Well, I won't be here,' retorted Fay. 'At least if you're agreeable, that is.'

'What do you mean?' asked Rose with interest.

'You know, we've no bookings for bed and breakfast for the next two weeks—everybody said it would be like that once the schools went back—so Joan's invited me to drive over to Dorset with her to go to little Michael's christening. Then we thought we'd stay on for a week or so and explore the countryside there.'

'Of course you must go,' urged Rose. 'If anybody does come, I'll manage perfectly well on my own, especially now that I've finished all the computer-programming work.'

'You're not going to take the job with that dreadful Martin, are you?' asked Fay with a hint of anxiety in her voice.

'No,' said Rose curtly.

Fay gave a sigh of relief. 'Well, you won't need to work at all if you marry Greg,' she said. 'Unless you want to, of course.'

'Mum! Nobody said anything about marriage.'

'Not yet, perhaps,' replied Fay shrewdly. 'But I saw it in the tea leaves only last night.'

Rose was inclined to believe the tea leaves were accurate, especially as the week wore on and Greg phoned her every day. Her mother and Joan Penwithick left on Monday, and each morning after that Rose was woken by the shrilling of the telephone and Greg's voice in her ear, deep and hoarse and sexy. 'Hello, Rose. I love you.' What a way to start the day! And then the flowers began arriving—a dozen red roses every morning. Rose was delirious with happiness until Thursday night, when something rather disturbing happened. Greg phoned quite late, just after she had climbed into bed.

'Rose? Greg here. You know how we agreed to meet at my place about six o'clock tomorrow night?'

'Yes?'

'Well, I'm up to my eyes in hassles with the shipyard right now, so I don't know if I can make it. In fact, I don't know if I can come down at all this weekend.'

'Oh, Greg!'

'I know, I know. I'll tell you what. Don't come over to my place. If I find I'm free after all, I'll phone you at your house. OK?'

'OK,' agreed Rose dismally.

'Good girl. I've got to fly now. Love you.'

And he rang off. All day Friday, Rose moped around the house, although she did cook a special dinner of chicken and almond casserole and cherry flan in case Greg arrived after all.

He didn't. At about ten-thirty, she ended up eating by herself and going morosely to bed. She was woken just before midnight by the shrilling of the phone.

'Greg?' she muttered blurrily.

'Yes, my love. Sorry, did I wake you? Just rang to say things are sorted out at work and I'm about to drive down. But don't come over tonight—it's too late. I'll catch up with you in the morning. All right?'

'Mm. All right,' agreed Rose blissfully, snuggling back under the covers. 'I love you, darling. Goodnight.'

But once she had hung up, Rose found it hard to get back to sleep. She tossed and turned and dozed briefly a couple of times only to dream of Greg and wake with a start. At about four o'clock, she gave an exclamation of disgust and flung back the covers.

'I don't care if it is late,' she announced defiantly. 'I'm going to go over to Greg's place anyway. As a matter of fact, I think I'll creep into his house and climb into bed with him. That will give him a surprise!'

Giggling softly, she dressed in a tracksuit, sprayed on a liberal squirt of Chanel No. 5 and went out to her car. Ten minutes later she turned into Greg's driveway, still feeling as high as a kite on excitement. But what she saw in the gleam of the headlights made her excitement vanish.

Parked in the driveway of Greg's house was Ingrid's pink sports car.

CHAPTER NINE

As IF in a dream, Rose pressed her feet down on the clutch and brake and she stopped dead, staring at the unwelcome sight in front of her. A light was showing through the curtains of Greg's bedroom, but otherwise there was no sign of life in the house. Suddenly the full force of what she was seeing struck her and she slumped over the steering-wheel and gave a low groan. An extraordinary succession of feelings swept through her. Shock, incredulity, dawning comprehension, rage. What could Ingrid be doing here at this hour of the morning? There was only one explanation she could think of and that was so hideous that it made her shake her head and murmur in a dazed, disjointed way, like someone trying to ward off a disaster that had already happened.

'No, no, no!' she said aloud and then gritted her teeth together to hold back a cry.

What should she do? Go inside and confront them? Her whole being recoiled at the thought. No, there was nothing she could do. Except retreat blindly like a wounded animal in search of shelter. How she got home she never knew, for she must have been driving by instinct. Certainly she had no conscious memory of it, until she parked her car in her own garage and stumbled inside her house. She spent the few remaining hours of darkness hopelessly pacing from room to room, in too much torment even to sit down, much less sleep. By morning a reaction had set in and she had suffered a desperate change of heart. There must be some reason for this, some explanation, something that would make it all right. As soon as it was light she got into her car again and drove back to Greg's cottage. But this time there was nobody there. Ingrid's pink car had vanished from the driveway and the house was silent and deserted. Fighting down a rising sense of panic, Rose drove back to her own home and with trembling fingers dialled the number of Greg's house in Plymouth. The phone rang and rang, but there was no reply. After that she called the shipyard, but nobody answered. The rest of the weekend passed in a sickening blur, with Rose giving vent to her restlessness by working furiously in the garden and the house. No bed-and-breakfast guests arrived, but there was no message from Greg either.

On Monday morning she phoned the shipyard again, but she did not get much joy from it. The receptionist put her through to Greg's secretary.

'Hello,' said Rose. 'This is Rose Ashley speaking. May I speak to Mr Trelawney, please?'

The secretary's tones came down the telephone line, cool, brisk and matter-of-fact. 'I'm sorry, Mr Trelawney has flown to Copenhagen and I don't know when he'll be back. He can't be contacted unless the matter is very urgent.'

Copenhagen! Rose almost reeled with shock. What on earth was Greg doing in Copenhagen? Of course, Copenhagen was the capital of Denmark, wasn't it?

'What about Miss Jensen, then?' she asked in a voice sharp with dismay. 'May I speak to her?'

'I'm sorry. Miss Jensen has gone to Copenhagen with Mr Trelawney. Is there any message I can give either of them when they come back?'

Gone with him! Then all her worst fears were realised. Ingrid had sworn she would succeed in winning Greg back and she had obviously done so. What possible message could Rose give either of them that would alleviate the horror she felt now?

'No, there's no message,' she said dully. 'Thank you for your help.'

Stunned, she put down the telephone. What was she to do? She felt as if her whole world was falling apart. Groping her way across the room as if she were blind, she found her bag and took out her car key. The enormity of what she had just learnt still had not fully penetrated and it was not until she was driving through the lush green countryside that at last the tears began to gather and roll down her cheeks. She wiped them silently away with the palm of her hand and kept on driving. She must have travelled for hours, visiting all the old haunts where she had gone with Greg—Talland Bay, Looe, Fowey, the spot near the cliff path where he had persuaded her to keep seeing him. Every cliff and wave and gorse bush seemed imprinted with his image and Rose gradually realised that she would have to leave Cornwall.

It was obvious now how badly she had been taken in by Greg. She had thought he loved her when all that he had been after was sex. Now that he had taken what he wanted from her, he had lost interest and gone off with Ingrid.

Angrily she forced herself to stop crying. This was a pain that went too deep for tears. It was not just hurt pride as it had been when Martin had left her. This time her whole world felt as if it was disintegrating. In spite of her protests over her mother's optimistic wedding plans, Rose had hoped to marry Greg. More important than that, she had hoped to spend the rest of her days with him, to share the joy of having children with him, to confront life's sorrows and challenges with him and, at the end of it all, to spend her old age in his company. Now all of that was snatched away from her and she felt as if she was nothing but an empty shell of the person she had once been. It was devastating, worse than devastating. She felt completely destroyed by his betrayal.

Yet she must make plans, she must get another job somewhere far away from here. She could never return to Cornwall, however much its beauty clutched at her heart. The memories were too painful.

But where was she to go? Not to Martin; she could not endure the humiliation of that. Still, there must be other companies that needed computer programmers. Perhaps she could find a cheap bedsitter in London and look for work there? But she would have to leave before Fay came back, for she simply could not endure the humiliation of revealing everything to her mother. And what about Greg? Should she write to him and explain her actions? Or maintain a dignified silence? It would be less painful to leave without any explanations at all, but the thought of Ingrid tormented her conscience. She had plenty of reason to hate the young Danish girl, yet she could not help feeling sorry for her. What sort of future did poor, foolish Ingrid have if Greg played the same deceitful tricks on her? Perhaps if Rose wrote and begged him not to do it, he might treat Ingrid more kindly. She drove back home, determined to try.

It cost her many sheets of crumpled notepaper before she was satisfied, and in the end her brief letter was the result of considerable heartache. Addressed simply to 'Greg'—she could not bring herself to write 'Dear Greg'—it said:

> I'm writing to tell you that everything is over between us. You see, I know the truth about you and Ingrid. When I was in Plymouth, I found something which proved you were having an affair with her. At the time, I refused to believe it. I told myself there must be some mistake. Now I realise that I was just being wilfully blind because I was taken in by your charm.

I believed all your lies, Greg. I even believed that I loved you until four a.m. on Saturday morning when I drove over to your house and saw Ingrid's car parked in your driveway. It's hard to believe that there was any innocent explanation for that and I'm tired of being deceived by you. So this is goodbye. I'm leaving Cornwall and I won't ever be coming back.

I've only one other thing to say to you. Please don't hurt that poor, vulnerable young girl as badly as you've hurt me.

Rose Ashley

After she had made her decision, Rose would have left immediately, but she had barely returned from mailing the letter to Greg when the telephone rang. Her spirits soared and then plummeted when she realised it was a business call—a charming elderly American couple wanting bed and breakfast for a few days while they went in search of their ancestral Cornish roots. Rose's mind was kept off her own problems a little bit by cooking, cleaning and planning itineraries for them. She kept half dreading and half hoping that Greg would phone, but he didn't. On Thursday morning she waved off her visitors with the sinking feeling that she really couldn't delay her departure any longer. Her mother was due back on Sunday, and if she wanted to avoid a lot of embarrassing questions she must leave soon. She decided she would go shopping in Looe, restock the kitchen and catch the train to London the following morning.

As she walked around the pretty little streets of West Looe she could hardly contain her misery. The bad weather had blown itself out and the sun was shining again, as warmly as if it were still midsummer, seagulls wheeled and shrieked overhead, housewives gossiped by the fresh-fruit barrows, fishermen ferried people across the river in dinghies and a few mothers and toddlers

played happily on the sands. Looking at it all, Rose was
suddenly smitten with a sharp pang of homesickness
before she had even left. She felt she belonged here as
surely as if she had lived in this beautiful place all her
life. And it was even worse on her way home when she
reached the road turning off to Polperro. The little village
was full of poignant memories for her and she suddenly
felt she had to take one last look at the tavern where she
had met Greg. Cursing her own ridiculous sentimentality, she left her car in the car park at the head of the
gorge and paid to ride down to the harbour in a horse-
drawn trap. Yes, there was the knitwear shop where she
had tried on the embroidered sweater, and there were
the twisting lanes leading to the Smuggler's Rest inn.
The postcards and souvenirs and advertisements for
cream teas still stood outside the tiny shops, although
there were fewer tourists now that the summer holidays
were finished. A thousand haunting memories assailed
her as she trailed pensively past the tubs of late petunias
and the quaint little antique shops towards the entrance
to the cliff path. As the whitewashed bulk of the tavern
loomed above her she caught her breath, half expecting
to find Greg inside. But when she pushed open the door
the dim interior of the bar was empty except for Jim the
barman, stolidly drying glasses.

'Hello, my love,' he exclaimed. 'Ee, you've timed
things badly today.'

Rose sighed. 'Why's that?' she asked without much
interest.

'Greg Trelawney was in here not an hour ago, looking
for you. Said he'd been to your house and no one was
home. Took on something terrible, he did. "If she comes
in here, you tell her I'll find her if I have to search every
inch of Cornwall for her!" Those were his very words.
Then he stormed out of here like a man possessed. I've

never seen Greg so upset in me life. Had a little tiff, have you, my love?'

Rose stood as if she were glued to the floor. For a moment she felt a treacherous rush of joy at the realisation that Greg had come looking for her. Then her joy was swept away with a rush of resentment. What if he had? It didn't change anything, did it? He probably just wanted to tell her another lot of lies, so that he could ensnare her all over again. Well, this time she was not going to be tricked. She must leave Cornwall and leave quickly before Greg could catch up with her. There was a train from Looe this afternoon at four twenty-three. If she hurried, she could still catch that.

'Thanks for telling me, Jim,' she said in a strained voice. 'Look, I must get home. If Greg comes back, don't mention that you've seen me.'

She retreated towards the door. Jim shook his head regretfully. 'Mad, the pair of them!' he announced to the glass he was drying. He called after Rose. 'Won't you even stop for lunch, my dear? I can do you a nice Cornish pasty.'

'Sorry!' cried Rose and then fled.

She hurried back to the car park so fast that her breath was coming in long, heaving gulps and her chest was burning as she reached it. If Greg had been to her home once already, surely he wouldn't go back there a second time? It should be safe for her to go home, shouldn't it? Her brain reeled with the thought of all the things she must do. Pack her bag, write a note to her mother, drive to Looe in time for the afternoon train and find somewhere safe to leave the car... She was in her bedroom, cramming her second suitcase shut when she heard the sound of the car in the driveway. An ominous sense of misgiving gripped her, then the back door opened. Rose ran to the head of the stairs.

'Mum? Is that you?' she called.

'No, it's me,' said a harsh masculine voice from down the stairs. 'And I want to know what's going on here.'

Rose's heart skipped a beat at the sight of Greg's thick, dark hair as he came striding up the stairs. Part of her mind registered that he was formally dressed in a houndstooth jacket, white shirt, red tie and grey trousers. Then she retreated to the bedroom and made a wild attempt to shut the door, but Greg thrust his foot in the gap.

'Go away!' she cried unsteadily.

'Not until you explain the meaning of this.' As he spoke he drew her crumpled letter out of the breast pocket of his jacket and waved it under her nose.

'It's obvious, isn't it?' she demanded. 'I found out you were sleeping with Ingrid and I didn't like being deceived.'

'I've never slept with Ingrid in my life!' snapped Greg. 'And you insult me by believing that I have.'

His denial was so heated that Rose almost believed him. His eyes were blazing feverishly and his unshaven face looked haggard and angry. For a moment she stood biting her lip in doubt but then the evidence came rushing back to torment her.

'Oh, come off it!' she cried bitterly. 'I saw her sports car outside your cottage at four o'clock in the morning last Saturday.'

'What of it?' he rasped.

'I suppose you have some innocent explanation for that, do you?' she demanded sarcastically.

'As a matter of fact, I do,' he snarled. 'Ingrid was at my place early on Saturday morning because of a crisis on one of the ships that I'd sold to her father's shipping company. There had been trouble with the steering mechanism earlier in the week, which is why I was delayed coming down to Cornwall in the first place. I thought everything was fixed up and then matters got worse. Because I didn't have a phone, Ingrid drove down to inform me. Then we both went up to London together and flew to Copenhagen to sort matters out.'

'What?' breathed Rose.

Greg paced stormily round the bedroom. 'I arrived back this morning from Denmark totally exhausted to find this,' he announced, brandishing the letter as if it were a deadly weapon. 'Accusing me of every kind of treachery imaginable. How could you believe such rubbish, Rose?'

She was taken aback, but after a moment she rallied. 'I didn't want to believe it, Greg,' she cried. 'But what else could I believe? Even if what you say this time is true, I know for certain that you've lied to me in the past, so how can I trust anything you say now? Besides, I happen to know you had an affair with Ingrid only a few months ago. I had proof of it.'

'That's clever of you, seeing that it never happened!' sneered Greg. 'What kind of proof did you have?'

'I found a prescription for contraceptive pills in Ingrid's name inside the bathroom cabinet of your bedroom,' Rose whipped back. 'I think it was reasonable to suppose that it was there because she was having an affair with you.'

Greg's face was suddenly ashen. 'You mean Ingrid really did get a prescription for the Pill?' he breathed. 'I thought it was all just bluff.'

'Greg, you're not making sense,' protested Rose. 'What do you mean, bluff? Anyway, one thing's obvious—you did sleep with her, didn't you?'

'No, I bloody didn't,' shouted Greg. 'Although it wasn't for want of trying on her part. I didn't want to tell you about it before because it was Ingrid's secret as much as mine.'

'She's already told me,' muttered Rose bitterly.

'Told you what?' asked Greg in a low, dangerous voice.

'That she stayed with you at your house, slept with you there. She told me you said you loved her and then turned against her and threw her out.'

'Damn her!' roared Greg. 'That girl is the biggest troublemaker in Western Europe.'

'What do you mean?' demanded Rose.

Greg unrolled the crumpled letter which he had crushed in his hands and read aloud from it. '"Poor, vulnerable young girl"!' he snorted. 'I could wring her vulnerable little neck!'

'Why, what's she done, apart from being exploited by you?' cried Rose.

'I'll tell you what she's done! She threw herself at me from the moment she arrived in England. Her father Erik is an old friend of mine and he asked me to have her over here as a favour so that she could learn about the shipbuilding. Apart from being my friend's daughter, she's only nineteen yeas old, so it's hardly likely I'd be callous enough to seduce her, is it? In any case, I had a housekeeper in my home as a chaperone so I thought she'd be safe enough. Well, it was safe enough for her, but I never thought about my own safety. Before she'd been in the house a week she convinced herself that she was madly in love with me and tried every trick in the book to get me to fall for her. When I didn't respond, she decided that perhaps fear of pregnancy was the reason for my lack of interest. She told me she'd go to a doctor and get herself fixed up. I warned her there and then that I'd send her back to Denmark on the next flight if I heard any more of it. Then I came home late one night and found her stark naked, sitting up in my bed. That was the end of it. I went to a hotel for the night and the next day I threw her out. I originally intended to make good my threat and send her back to Denmark, and I wish to heaven I had, but she talked me into letting her stay on here in England. I found her a flat in Plymouth and she's been living there ever since. Now do you see why I didn't want you to know of this? Can you imagine how embarrassed Ingrid would be in a few years' time if anyone apart from me hears about it?'

Rose winced. 'Yes,' she admitted slowly. 'If she really did go to those lengths to try to get you, she'll cringe over it once she meets a man she really does care about. All the same, it's hard to believe she could ever have been so foolish.'

A muscle twitched in Greg's check. 'Hard to believe,' he muttered under his breath. 'Yes, and if I don't do something to convince you, you never will fully believe it, will you? The shadow of doubt will always lie between us and ruin things for sure. Well, I'm not going to put up with it. Ingrid is going to have to tell you the truth herself.' He strode purposefully across the room.

'What are you going to do?' asked Rose.

'Phone Ingrid and demand that she tell you herself what really happened. With luck she might actually do so. While we were in Denmark she met a young engineer called Karl Svensen on board the ship we were inspecting and the atmosphere between them was getting positively steamy. As a matter of fact, I wouldn't be surprised if she decided to stay on in Copenhagen with him permanently. I suspect dear Ingrid is beginning to see me as a geriatric has-been.'

Picking up the phone with a murderous expression, he punched in the number and waited impatiently.

'Ingrid? This is Greg. Would you be good enough to tell Rose the whole truth about your relationship with me? I might add that I am deeply in love with her, so it's very important to me that she knows what really happened between us. Here she is now.'

There was a nervous giggle at the other end of the line. 'Oops! Rose, is that you? I suppose I'd better admit right now that what I told you in Plymouth wasn't exactly the truth. You see, I wanted Greg to sleep with me and I thought maybe he was afraid of being a daddy and that was why he wouldn't, so I went to the doctor and got those pills. It was just a waste of time, though, because Greg only shouted at me and threw me out... but he did let me get dressed first. I went in such a hurry that I left the prescription form behind. When you found it, that gave me a great idea. I could see Greg was already falling in love with you and I was very jealous of you. I thought maybe if I could make you sorry for me, you wouldn't go to bed with him. So I told you a few little white lies.'

'Little white lies,' breathed Rose, raising her eyes to the ceiling.

'Are you very cross with me?' asked Ingrid fearfully.

'If you weren't several hundred miles away, I'd murder you,' vowed Rose.

'There's no need!' carolled Ingrid with a sudden giggle. 'I've lost interest in Greg now anyway. He's awfully old, isn't he? And there's an engineer who works for my father called Karl—tall, blond, utterly yummy! I don't think I'll let you meet him, Rose; maybe you'll tear all your clothes off and jump in his bed. No, only joking. Listen, do you forgive me?'

Rose gave a groan of laughter. 'I suppose so.'

'Good. Then give me back to Greg.' There was the sound of a large, juicy kiss and a tinny voice coming down the line. 'Bye, Greg. Make sure you invite Karl and me to the wedding!'

'Well?' said Greg sternly as he hung up the phone. 'Are you convinced?'

Rose heaved a long, shaky sigh of mingled embarrassment and relief. 'Yes,' she admitted. 'I'm sorry I ever doubted you, Greg.'

'So you should be,' he growled. 'Seeing I fell in love with you the first moment I saw you.'

Rose let out a soft gasp. 'I don't believe you,' she murmured uncertainly, but there was a rising note of hope in her voice.

'It's true,' insisted Greg. 'Well, almost true. Let's say I was intrigued from the first moment I met you. At first you could have been any pretty woman with big blue eyes and an appealing smile. But there was something in your manner that I found irresistible. Perhaps it was the way you darted about like a worried little bird and that mixture of shyness and sophistication. Anyway, once I'd spent an evening in your company, I knew that you attracted me more than any woman I had ever met. I wanted you so badly I couldn't think about anything else, and it wasn't only physical, either. I was drawn to you emotionally. When you confided in me about what Martin had done to you I was so furious that I wanted to flatten the swine. I hated to think of anybody hurting you and deceiving you like that.'

'And yet you lied to me yourself,' Rose reminded him.

Greg looked uncomfortable. 'I know, and I've regretted it ever since because of the way it came between us. But I never intended to hurt you with it, Rose. At first it was just a joke to go along with the assumptions you'd made about me. I meant to tell you the truth that same evening and I thought you would probably find it funny too. Then, after you confided in me about Martin, I couldn't bring myself to do it. Somehow the whole atmosphere had changed, had become terribly tense and emotional, and it would have seemed like a slap in the face to you. Besides, you were so vehement about your hatred for rich men that I didn't dare do it for fear of losing you. I thought if we could spend some more time together you could get to know me and like me. Perhaps you'd even begin to feel the same unsettling, roller-coaster ride of emotions that I experienced with you.'

'I did,' admitted Rose unwillingly. 'From the first moment I met you.'

'Did you?' asked Greg urgently. 'I thought you did, but I wasn't sure. You were so cool, so adept at hiding your feelings, and yet something was lurking in your eyes that made me suspect it was the same for you as it was for me. I probably should have told you the truth about myself that day at Talland Bay, but it was so magical just being there with you that I didn't want to spoil it by risking a row. And then Hugh came over to my house and split the beans anyway.'

'Would you really have slept with me if he hadn't?' asked Rose.

Greg sighed. 'I honestly don't know. I don't think so; I can't believe that I would have gone to such lengths without having matters clear between us. But you must understand this, Rose: I didn't take you back to my cottage with the intention of going to bed with you that night anyway. But things got out of hand, I was swept along by the force of my need for you. And it wasn't just a physical need, either, although I won't deny the power of that, my love. When I think of the softness of your body, your voice, the smell of your skin that night... But it wasn't only that. By that time I was half crazy with wanting you as a person too. I liked your funny mixture of prissiness and daring, your intelligence, your dry sense of humour, the way you were so earnest about providing for your mother and paying back your bank loan and keeping your head held high. I was more than half in love with you, although I'd barely known you a week and I was up to my eyes in trouble of my own making with you. Then old Hugh blundered in and delivered my death blow by telling you the truth!'

Rose snorted. 'Well, you returned from the dead pretty smartly! All those bunches of flowers...and then booking into our cottage as a paying guest! I had no idea it was going to be you. My mother told me it was a mysterious stranger who'd suffered some terrible crisis in love.'

'Well, I had,' insisted Greg plaintively.

Rose tried hard to maintain her severe expression, but suddenly her lips began to twitch. 'Oh, Greg, you are a wretch!' she cried. 'I don't know how you ever persuaded me to give you a second chance.'

Never one to miss a promising opportunity, Greg put his arms around her and drew her hard against him. Her heart gave a wild lurch and began to hammer furiously at the intoxicating masculine strength of his hands, at the spicy aroma of his skin, at the urgency she saw glinting in his dark, stormy eyes.

'Perhaps it was because you realised that I had fallen deeply and hopelessly in love with you and wouldn't rest until I made you my wife,' he replied with unaccustomed earnestness.

Her breath caught in her throat. 'Oh, Greg,' she whispered uncertainly. 'You can't mean——'

'I do mean it, Rose. I knew that day on the cliff-top when we agreed to be friends that friendship would never be enough for me. I wanted you, body and soul, as my wife, my companion, the mother of my children, the centre of my existence.'

'But you were always so scathing about marriage. That day in the churchyard at Talland, you said you didn't think you'd ever marry.'

'So did you,' he reminded her. 'It made me furious and I couldn't work out why. Then I realised how serious my feelings towards you must be.'

'Then why didn't you tell me sooner?' she burst out.

'I was afraid that you would think that I was leading you on exactly the way Martin had done just so I could get you into bed with me,' he replied. 'Then when Martin himself showed up, I suffered agonies of jealousy. I was afraid you were still in love with him, but you weren't, were you?'

'You know I wasn't,' exclaimed Rose. 'I would never have made love with you if I had been.'

His hands sought hers and gripped them hard. 'I know, I know,' he agreed exultantly. 'And when you did I was walking on air. At last it looked as if everything was going right for me. I intended to come down and propose to you the following weekend, until all that trouble with the ship blew up. I still can't believe that you thought I'd stoop so low as to seduce Ingrid when I had already told you I loved you.'

'Greg, I'm sorry!' cried Rose remorsefully. 'Will you ever forgive me?'

Greg looked doubtful. His black eyebrows met in a scowl, his eyes narrowed sternly and his mouth set in a forbidding line. 'I might,' he growled. 'On one condition.'

'What's that?' asked Rose, torn between hope and misgiving.

'That you promise to marry me as soon as possible and never, ever doubt again that I love you.'

Rose gave a gasp of joy and hurled herself at him. 'Oh, Greg. Yes, yes!'

There was a long silence, punctuated only by sighs and murmurs, till at last Rose lifted her head and gazed at Greg, her eyes brimming with joy. 'Can we be married in Talland church?' she asked.

'Yes. And afterwards a long cruise might be fun. The Mediterranean, perhaps, or Florida. Or we could go to Hong Kong.'

'Anywhere,' said Rose fervently. 'As long as I'm with you.'

'And after that,' said Greg, 'it'll be back to work in Plymouth with our weekends here in Polperro. You can work or not as you please, my love, but I hope you'll want to have my children and have them soon.'

'I will,' whispered Rose huskily, her eyes shining. 'Greg, darling, I will.'

'It's all settled, then, isn't it?' he demanded.

There was more ecstatic kissing and sighing until at last Rose nestled against his shoulder. 'Nearly,' she agreed dreamily. 'Greg, when do you want to get married?'

'Tomorrow.'

She pinched him. 'Seriously.'

'June would be nice,' said Greg reflectively.

Rose's eyes widened. That was exactly what her mother had suggested!

'Just as a matter of interest, what do you think I should wear at the wedding?' she asked.

Greg looked taken aback. 'How about a long white satin dress with little pearls on it?' he suggested. 'And perhaps you could have the bridesmaids in a sort of orangey pink?'

Rose started to laugh. She laughed so hard that she almost choked. 'Tell me, do you read tea leaves?' she spluttered at last.

'Tea leaves?' echoed Greg in a baffled voice.

'Never mind, darling,' murmured Rose, swallowing a final giggle and rising on tiptoe to kiss him. 'I'll tell you all about it after the wedding.'

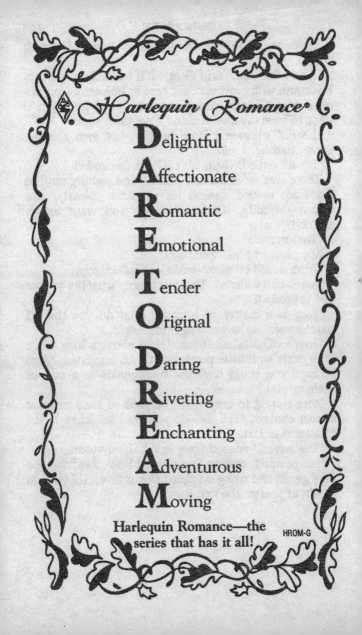

Harlequin Romance®

Delightful
Affectionate
Romantic
Emotional

Tender
Original

Daring
Riveting
Enchanting
Adventurous
Moving

Harlequin Romance—the
series that has it all!

HROM-G

LOOK FOR OUR FOUR FABULOUS MEN!

Each month some of today's bestselling authors bring
four new fabulous men to Harlequin American Romance.
Whether they're rebel ranchers, millionaire power brokers
or sexy single dads, they're all gallant princes—and
they're all ready to sweep you into lighthearted fantasies
and contemporary fairy tales where anything is possible
and where all your dreams come true!

You don't even have to make a wish...
Harlequin American Romance will grant your every desire!

Look for Harlequin American Romance
wherever Harlequin books are sold!

HARLEQUIN PRESENTS®

HARLEQUIN PRESENTS
men you won't be able to resist
falling in love with...

HARLEQUIN PRESENTS
women who have feelings
just like your own...

HARLEQUIN PRESENTS
powerful passion in
exotic international settings...

HARLEQUIN PRESENTS
intense, dramatic stories that will keep you
turning to the very last page...

HARLEQUIN PRESENTS
The world's bestselling romance series!